MW00613927

Written by a parent for parents, this book is both an emotional comfort and a practical guide. The focus on boots and bars is an informative and much needed resource for this essential part of clubfoot treatment that is literally in the hands of parents and caregivers. I would recommend it for all families who are beginning their child's clubfoot journey.

-Karen Mara Moss

(Founder and Executive director of Steps South Africa, clubfoot parent)

*Tips for Helping Your **Clubfoot Cutie** During Treatment*

CLUBFOOT CHRONICLES

MAUREEN HOFF

published by

Clubfoot Chronicles

Copyright © 2021 by Maureen Hoff. All rights reserved. No part of this publication of this publication may be reproduced, distributed or transmitted in any form or by any means, including photocopying, recording, or other electronic or mechanical methods, without the prior written permission of the publisher, except in the case of brief quotations embodied in critical reviews and certain other noncommercial uses permitted by copyright law. Requests for permission should be addressed to:

MD Orthopaedics
604 North Parkway Street,
Wayland, Iowa 52654
info@mdorthopaedics.com

ISBN 978-0-578-89063-0

Design by Brent Spurlock, Berryville, AR
Cover photos by Ellie Grace Photography, Broomfield, CO
Illustrations by Tom Billups, MD Orthopaedics
Selected photos by Erin Deuitch Photography, Denver, CO
Bar Cover on cover image by 26thAve Clubfoot Essentials

Printed in the United States of America

www.mdorthopaedics.com

Dedicated to:

My beloved husband & three amazing girls

Contents

INTRODUCTION

How To Utilize This Book

My youngest daughter was born with bilateral clubfoot in 2018. I can distinctly remember the day after my ultrasound as a day of personal transformation. I had a million questions swirling through my head — what would treatment look like, where would I find the right doctor to perform the treatment, where could I find all the information I needed about clubfoot, and how would I possibly care for an infant going through medical treatment while trying to care for my other children? I didn't have answers for any of the questions at that moment, but I remember feeling that I would somehow figure it out. I had this overwhelming feeling that my life had changed the moment we heard the diagnosis and that I would become a different person moving forward. And that is exactly what happened. While researching treatment options, interviewing medical professionals, calling insurance companies, and searching the internet for anything clubfoot related, I changed in ways I never knew I could. The change was not always easy, as change usually isn't, but it made me a stronger person.

My goal in writing this book is to provide other clubfoot parents with support, encouragement, and information while they are on their treatment journey with their children. The focus of the book is to provide necessary practical information and product recommendations, as well as sharing my personal experience caring for my cutie to help you feel supported throughout your journey. Clubfoot treatment is not a quick fix, and most of the hard labor is placed on the caregiver's shoulders, so it is vital that you feel supported during your child's clubfoot treatment. While there will be moments of frustration and exhaustion, clubfoot is a treatable birth defect, meaning if you stay the course and put in the work, your child will have fully functional pain-free feet when you are finished. This book is here to support you through the difficult moments and celebrate all of your hard work caring for your precious child.

It was my goal to divide the book into sections, so you could easily access topics based on your needs. You will find product recommendations that worked for us, as well as products compiled from other clubfoot resources and parents. Product recommendations are divided by section, i.e., sleep products are in the sleep section and BnB accessories are in the BnB section. All products referenced herein are not endorsed by the book but are simply included because they worked for us. If a price is listed it was relevant at the time of publishing.

Emotional Focus

I received my master's degree in Marriage and Family therapy in 2012, a few months before my eldest daughter was born. Because of this, I not only place tremendous value on the physical aspect of treating your child with clubfoot, but the emotional aspects as well. In several sections of this book I highlight my own emotional process, and I encourage you to explore your emotional process as well. I believe that it is vital for all of us to have the courage to explore the emotional impact of challenging experiences. I can promise you that there will be at least a few difficult moments during your journey. It is my belief that you and your family will benefit from taking time to explore these emotions in the hope that you will grow stronger in the process.

Cutie

I made the decision to refer to my daughter as "cutie" rather than use her actual name throughout the book for two reasons. The first is to honor her privacy and allow her to tell her story in her own way, in her own time. This book is about my caring for a child during BnB treatment, and while it is heavily focused on my daughter and her treatment, it is ultimately my story. I do not speak for her or pretend to understand what having clubfoot is like. If my daughter chooses to tell her story at some point, (maybe when she can actually talk?) then I'd like to leave that choice entirely to her. This is the same reason I chose not to share her story on any social media, because it is simply not my story to tell.

The second is to generalize the experience for anyone who has a cutie of their own. While this book is about our personal experience, it is also a reference guide for caretakers providing treatment for their own clubfoot cuties. My hope is by generalizing the experience with a general term, it will be more relatable for all readers.

Quick Clubfoot Facts

Clubfoot is a deformity of the foot which cases the foot to be twisted and pointed up and inwards towards the ankle.

- 1 in 1000 babies in the USA are born with clubfoot.

- Clubfoot is one of the most common birth defects.

- Clubfoot is only serious if left untreated.

- There is no known cause for congenital clubfoot.

- The Ponseti method is the most widely used mode of treatment for clubfoot.

- The earlier a child is treated to correct clubfoot, the easier and more successful the treatment can be.

- Clubfoot is a multifactorial trait, meaning that there are many factors involved in causing a birth defect, some environmental and some genetic.

- Many famous athletes were born with clubfoot such as Mia Hamm, Kristie Yamaguchi, & Troy Aikman.

Medical Disclaimer

This book is not meant to replace any medical advice nor should any information in this book replace guidance from your doctor. The information compiled is from personal clubfoot experiences. Doctors and other medical professionals may have differing opinions about the course of treatment for your cutie. This book is not a substitute for professional medical advice. Please consult your doctor with any questions, as every clubfoot situation and every clubfoot child's treatment plan may differ slightly.

CHAPTER 1

UNDERSTANDING PONSETI METHOD

THE FIRST STAGE OF TREATMENT is clubfoot correction through serial casting. This chapter will explain the preferred method of treatment, as well as our experience and things that worked for us.

Discussed Topics:

- The Start of Our Journey
- About the Ponseti Method and Resources
- Clubfoot Treatment Timeline
- Our Casting Journey
- Tips for Casting Appointments
- Red Flags During Casting
- Product Recommendations

The Start of Our Journey

The first time I heard the term clubfoot, I was 22 weeks pregnant when we had our anatomy ultrasound. I was carrying my third child (my husband and I have 2 older girls neither of whom had the diagnosis.) Our ultrasound tech scanned through our child's brain, heart, lungs, and abdomen before she said she saw something in the feet that she would come back to later in the scan. She noted that the feet looked turned inwards, but that babies are very bendy, and it could have simply been the position that our baby was lying in at that moment.

I remember that in this initial moment of diagnosis the word clubfoot was mentioned, prior to our tech moving on with the scan. For the remainder of the scan, I was dead silent. I didn't say another word. My husband kept looking at me asking if I was okay, but I couldn't speak. If you have ever had a conversation with me you will know that I am rarely at a loss for words, so my silence spoke volumes. All I could think about was that there was something wrong with my baby. Not knowing what clubfoot meant, I kept picturing my baby without any toes, like a golf club. I thought it meant that our baby would have deformed feet that would not allow her to walk or even stand.

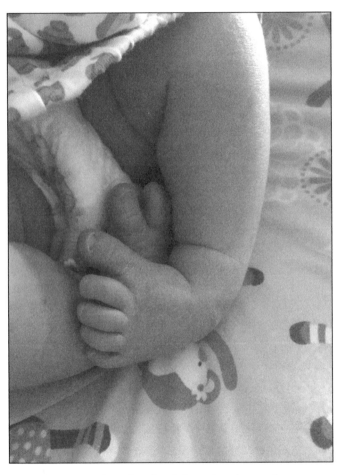

A picture of my daughter's feet after she was born.

I didn't know what clubfoot was or have a family history of it (that I knew of at the time; turns out several people in my mom's extended family have it), so I was imagining the worst possible outcome. So, there I was, lying in the now extensive ultrasound, to confirm that nothing else looked irregular. I kept thinking that this couldn't be real. I felt certain the tech would circle back to the feet and say something like, "your baby has moved, and the feet look in normal position now."

But that didn't happen. When the tech did circle back, it was to confirm what she had seen earlier. She then went on to explain that she could see both the foot and shin bone in the same image, which meant that the foot was curled in. Otherwise you would have seen the shin bone and then the bottom of foot in two separate images. She then brought us in to see the doctor, who further explained the diagnosis, and I continued to reel from the shock and cry hysterically throughout.

Before the moment of diagnosis, I knew nothing about clubfeet. I had never even heard the word before. I went from knowing absolutely nothing, to writing a book about Boots and Bar (BnB) treatment in a year's time. I wrote this book to provide you with a resource to understand and help you through the most labor-intensive portion of your child's treatment. To help you understand that you can go from knowing nothing about a subject to mastering that subject within a short timeframe. You will live it, walk it, and experience every day with your baby, and you will become a master.

As parents, we will do anything to help ensure our child has their best shot at a healthy and happy life, and the clubfoot treatment is no different. You will do it because you have to. You will put those boots on five times a day because you have to. You will do it because there is no other choice. Well I suppose that's not entirely true, because you could choose not to. You could choose to be lax about treatment and not take it seriously. But I hope that you choose to show up. Just like I choose to show up every day for my daughter's treatment. I choose to perform her physical therapy and put her BnB on religiously, every day, without exception. I choose to research as much information as my brain could handle. I continue to choose this every day because I choose my daughter's sweet feet every day! I am confident that you will too. You are stronger than you know, and you and your baby will make progress.

You just have to choose to show up.

About the Ponseti Method and Resources

When we heard our daughter would be born with clubfoot, we immediately started to think about what her treatment would be. Our OB who made the diagnosis gave us a very brief overview of what treatment would look like and mentioned that there would be serial casting involved, but that was the extent of the information she provided. While we felt a lot of fear about the diagnosis of clubfoot, we were desperate to find information about how we could successfully treat her, and this was how our research on the Ponseti Method began. For the remaining four months of my pregnancy I spent countless hours researching treatment options and this section provides a brief overview of the medical information I gathered and found helpful. This is a condensed overview of treatment and is not meant to replace any further research you do or the medical information provided by your clubfoot doctor.

The Ponseti Method is without a doubt the most effective and successful form of treatment for clubfoot children. The basics of the treatment include serial casting, which will gently manipulate the foot into the correct position and bracing up to age of 4 or 5 years old. The goal is that casting gets the feet into the corrected position and the brace maintains that correction. The casting part of treatment is crucial because it sets up the success of the bracing in the later years. If the casting doesn't correct the feet, the bracing won't work. It is vital that you do your research about casting and the doctor you choose to perform it because it is the crux of the clubfoot treatment.

Serial casting means that a cast is applied weekly, for approximately 6-8 weeks. I know of one doctor who provides an accelerated casting schedule, meaning a new cast is applied every 3-5 days, with the same amount of success, but typically the cast will be taken off and reapplied weekly. The first cast is usually applied when your baby is approximately 2 weeks old. Occasionally the first cast will be applied later if the baby is a preemie or too small to apply the first cast. I have read most doctors want the baby to be at least 7 pounds, but that is a judgement call by your cutie's doctor.

The doctor will gradually stretch the babies' foot into the correct position and a plaster cast will be placed from toes to hip to keep the correction in place. The treatment is performed at a young age to take advantage of the child's elasticity of the tissues that form the ligaments and joint capsules, which allows for bringing the displaced bones into the correct position (www.uichildrens.org/health-library/parents-children-born-clubfeet). Simply put, your baby is flexible and malleable at a young age which makes it easier for the doctor to stretch the foot into the correct position with minimal discomfort. Not to mention your sweet newborn is not mobile at all yet, which makes caring for them simpler because they are not moving and grooving every chance they get.

It is super important to note that the Ponseti method should always be considered prior to any surgical treatment. With any sort of surgery there is a considerably high chance of scarring, stiffness, and muscle weakness which can cause pain as your child grows. About 80% of clubfoot children will need a small surgical procedure called a tenotomy once their foot has reached the correct position. This means that the Achilles' tendon will be severed completely by a small incision performed by your doctor, and a final cast will be put on to allow the tendon to heal completely. The reason for this procedure is flexibility. While the casting can gently move the foot into the correct position, if the Achilles' tendon is short and tight, your cutie's flexibility will be negatively impacted. This final cast will be on for approximately 14-21 days, which your doctor should discuss with you prior to the procedure.

Finally, after all casting and tenotomy are completed, the child will enter into a brace wearing phase called Boots and Bar. This entails the feet being placed in boots that are connected by a stable bar that keep the feet in the accurate degree of correction. The BnB has several stages of wear, starting with full time wear of 23-hours a day for a set number of months and gradually decreasing and ending with 12-hour nightly wear until the age of 4 or 5.

The success rate of the Ponseti method for clubfoot treatment is 95%, which is incredible. Meaning 95% of the time, without any major surgery, your cutie will have corrected and pain free feet. Yes, it can feel like a long haul, it is not the quick fix of a surgery and recovery, and certainly not a one and done situation, but there is a huge glowing light at the end of the tunnel that is your child's best possible chance at a pain free, fully active and functioning life.

Obviously, I passionately believe that the Ponseti method is the best mode of treatment for the correction of clubfoot. And while this book does not extensively address the casting portion of treatment, I do assume that the parents reading along have chosen to follow this method and have either completed or plan to complete the casting phase before moving on to BnB.

There are ample resources available to research the Ponseti method and confirm why it is the best mode of treatment for your little one. If you are looking for more detailed information about the Ponseti method, a list of doctors who use Ponseti, as well as interview questions to ask any potential healthcare provider please consider the following resources:

- The Parent's Guide to Clubfoot - Betsy Miller (Hunter House Inc, Publishers; 2012)

- Clubfoot: The Quest for a Better Life for Millions of Children – Thomas M. Cook (Ice Cube Press, LLC; 2019)

- Clubfoot C.A.R.E.S. – (http://www.clubfootcares.org)

- Clubfoot Hub- (https://www.clubfoothub.com)

- St. Louis Children's Hospital- (https://www.stlouischildrens.org)

- University of Iowa Stead Family Children's Hospital- (https:// uichildrens.org/medical-services/clubfoot)

- Ponseti International- (www.ponseti.info)

These helpful resources can be referred to throughout your child's clubfoot journey. I frequented the resources listed above prior to having my daughter, while choosing a doctor, and throughout treatment for various tips and answers to my many questions. This is by no means an exhaustive list, and I'm sure you'll find additional resources when doing your own research. These are simply the few that I used the most.

Casting Treatment Timeline

Although individual cases vary, here is the basic clubfoot treatment timeline:

- Baby diagnosed with clubfoot in ultrasound (at approximately 20 weeks)

- Research doctors well-versed in Ponseti method

- Schedule consultation(s) with doctors

- Choose your doctor and get treatment information

  o How to schedule first appointment?

  o What to bring to first appointment?

- Baby is born (hooray!)
- Call doctor to set up first cast when home from hospital
- Schedule first cast per doctor, approximately around baby's two-week mark
- Schedule 14-day blood screen prior to first cast (usually with pediatrician or in lab in hospital setting)
- Two weeks old - first cast
- Three weeks - second cast
- Four weeks - third cast
- Five weeks - fourth cast
- Six weeks - fifth cast (possible tenotomy; our cuties happened one week later)
- Seven weeks - sixth cast (tenotomy for us)
- Ten weeks - last cast removed - transition to BnB
- 23-hour BnB wear for 3 months (equivalent of 14 weeks)
- Five-six months - gradual transition to 18-hour wear
- Nine months - transition to 14-16-hour wear
- 12 months - 12-hour wear mark
- 1 year to 4 or 5 years - 12-hour wear consistently.

Our Casting Journey

While this book largely focuses on BnB treatment, I thought it would be helpful to provide some information about our journey, helpful items that we used, and various tips from the medical community.

Our cutie had her first cast put on at 13 days old, at our local children's hospital, by a doctor whom we had met and interviewed during my pregnancy. We were prepared for the casting appointment and for what our casting experience would mainly entail through our personal research and consultation with our doctor. My biggest recommendation to prepare yourselves and your cutie for this phase of treatment is to meet your doctor, research their experience with the Ponseti method, and ask any and all questions you might have. I think I had a list of over 75 questions for our doctor. I broke the list down into different sections to ensure I had an exhaustive list of any question I might have.

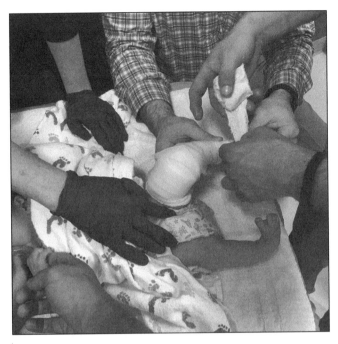

1.1 Our cutie's first casting appointment.

I created this list by researching through the websites mentioned above and then added questions of my own. I encourage you to make your own list as well. Bring it with you, and don't be afraid to ask any question on that list. As I will go into detail about later in this book, there was one answer to one question that stuck with me and inevitably helped make the decision to switch doctors. The websites have lists of questions that you can ask in your consultation, so bring one of those if you don't know the right questions to ask.

It is important to research and ask these questions because casting is the most important part of your child's treatment. It will "make or break" your clubfoot treatment. You want a doctor who has extensive experience with the Ponseti method, because while it does not involve a major surgery, an inexperienced doctor can make your cutie's clubfoot complex, and treatment can become more involved and prolonged. The Ponseti method has specific guidelines that must be followed in order to fully correct your child's feet. It may seem that any doctor can cast a baby's foot into a different position, but you only have to join a clubfoot social media group to realize all the things that can go wrong (more on this in Chapter 10 Finding the Right Support). So, it is vital that you find a doctor who can provide adequate care for your child because you could end up having to redo a portion of treatment, or worse end up with a complicated case caused by mistreatment. At the consultation be prepared to ask whatever questions you have. This will be one of your first opportunities to advocate for your cutie during their clubfoot treatment journey.

Our cutie has bilateral clubfoot and had six casts in total, with a tenotomy on both heels prior to her last cast, which she had for 2 ½ weeks. By-and-large, our casting experience was rather smooth. Our cutie adjusted fairly well to the casts and never seemed to be in any unbearable pain. Her biggest adjustments were on the nights of a new cast. She hated the coldness of the plaster as they were setting and wanted to be held most of the night. (Ponseti method recommends plaster casts as they provide a more stable environment for the foot.) We held her those nights and made sure a blanket was covering her casts. She was usually sleeping on one of our chests as the body heat provided the most warmth. Usually by the next morning the casts were fully dry, and she would return to normal. At the end of this chapter I will provide a list of products that we used and helped us during the casting phase in hopes that you will find something that assists you and your cutie during this time.

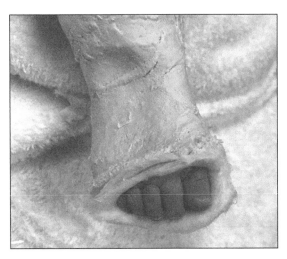

1.2 Our cutie's toes in the plaster cast.

Tips for casting appointments:

- Bring a bottle - With formula or breast milk. This bottle can be used to help calm your cutie while the cast is being applied. I brought a bottle to every appointment but never ended up using one. Some doctors are also comfortable with you breastfeeding your cutie while the cast is being applied, as long as you are comfortable. I waited until the casts were applied to feed my cutie as that worked best for our routine. You can work with your doctor to figure out the best routine for you and your cutie.

- Bring your own bath stuff - The hospital will provide you with bath wash and rags, but we always felt more comfortable bringing our own. It made the experience a little more personal, as this is the only true bath your cutie will get each week. Some doctors may not provide a bath during the casting appointment, so check with your doctor to determine if bringing bath stuff is appropriate.

- Bring the old casts home - Even if you don't think you will want or use them in the future, bring the old casts home. You can wrap them in a receiving blanket so that plaster doesn't get everywhere. My husband saved the day with this as he grabbed the casts. I was way too distracted trying to make my cutie as comfortable as possible.

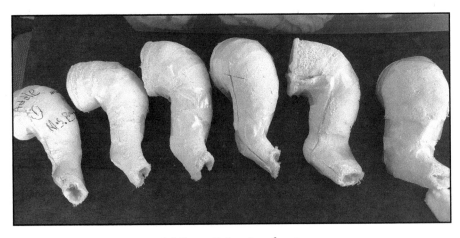

1.3 Our cutie's series of casts.

- Use a permanent marker - We used a permanent marker to draw a line across the toes where the cast ended. This would help us ensure that the cast had not slipped. The marker washed off easily during the bath the following week.

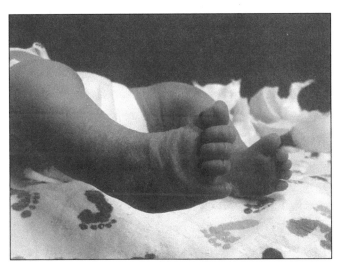

1.4 The permanent marker line on our cutie's foot after cast was removed and before her bath.

- Bring leg warmers - Put new leg warmers on after the casts are applied. They help keep the casts from either bumping into each other (bilateral) or from scratching the non-casted leg (unilateral). We left the first pair of leg warmers overnight and then switched them the morning after the cast was applied. The casts usually take 24 hours to completely set (http://www.ponseti.info/casting-care-instructions.html).

  The leg warmers are also great for protecting your cutie's casts from getting wet or any diaper leakage.

- Bring a receiving blanket/muslin blanket - We rolled up the blankets and tucked it under the knees of the casts in the car seat during the trip home. This helps support the knees by providing padding and can add comfort for your cutie.

- Use Tylenol for pain relief - We brought infant Tylenol to every appointment but only needed it the night after her tenotomy.

Your pediatrician or casting doctor can help you figure out the correct dosage for your cutie.

- Take pictures - Take as many pictures as you can. Take them of the doctor applying the cast, of your cutie in the bath (wet babies are so cute!), and of the casts after they have been applied. We took close-up photos of the toes of each cast that was applied to use as a reference at home to double check the casts hadn't slipped. We also took progress photos each week. After the casts were removed, we took photos of the progress of our cutie's feet. It was amazing to see the amount of progress her feet made each week.

- Bring noise blocking headphones - We didn't have these, but if you do you can use them for when your cutie's casts are being removed. The cast saw is loud and can been startling for babies, so the headphones help to ease the stress. The cast removal process was the only time our cutie cried during the casting appointments. The noise was loud and the sensation of air on her sensitive skin would set her off.

- Ask lots of questions - Don't be afraid to ask questions about how your cutie's treatment is going and how the feet are progressing. Your doctor is there to help your child and make you feel confident that their feet are being corrected. If your doctor is not willing to answer your questions or is not giving you the responses that you feel are adequate, don't give up. Keep asking questions, especially if you have any concerns about the treatment, because your parental gut will never steer you wrong. As our current doctor says, if you think everything looks good then it probably is. But if you think something is wrong, you should follow that instinct. My husband said this was the most stressful part of the casting phase, trusting the doctor to correct our cutie's feet. It didn't help that our doctor was not great with answering our questions (more on this in Chapter 3: Working with Doctors).

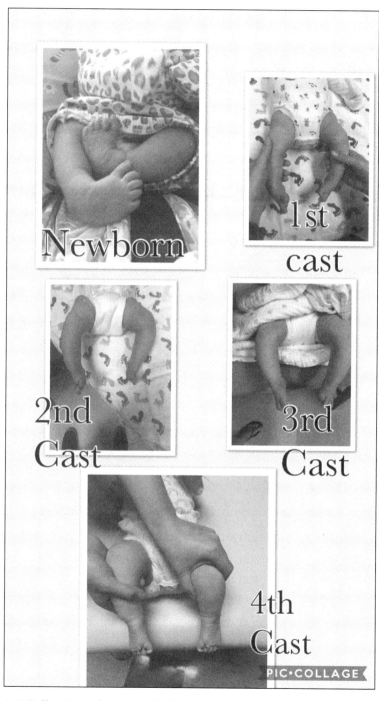

1.5 Collection of our cutie's feet progression after each cast.

Red Flags to Look for During Casting

The casting process is precise, and there are warning signs that things are not going as planned. You can watch out for these potential problems when your cutie is in this stage of treatment. The list below is not exhaustive but will give you a brief overview of what to watch out for. If you need more information about any of the items below, please contact your medical professional or reference the websites above for more detailed information.

- Slipped casts - A slipped cast is when your child's foot slips up into the cast and loses its correct position. This is a serious issue that needs to be remedied by a medical professional immediately. The slipped cast will need to be removed and new cast applied immediately in order to maintain the position of the foot. You will know if the cast has slipped because the babies' toes will change positions in the cast, usually slipping further up into the cast. The baby's toes should always be visible in every cast. In order to ensure the cast has not slipped you can mark the toes with a permanent maker and also take pictures of the toes when the cast was first applied to refer back to if you think there has been any movement.

  We did not experience a slipped cast on our journey but had fellow cuties that did. Slipped casts should not be a common occurrence, and if it is repeatedly happening during your cutie's treatment, you will want to get a second opinion from another doctor to ensure damage is not being done to your child's feet.

- Blanching of toes - The plaster casts used for clubfoot treatment are heavy and need to be tight enough to keep the child's foot securely in place, but not so tight that it impacts circulation of the toes. The toes should be able to blanch, meaning that when you press down on them, they will turn from pink to white and then back to pink again. If the toes are not doing this, then you need to call your doctor immediately as the casts may be too tight and causing circulation issues. Cutting off circulation to the toes is a major issue as well and can cause damage to the toes.

The only time we experienced issues with circulation was directly after a cast was applied and her toes stayed white for a few minutes before they turned pink again. We made sure the doctor came back in to check the toes and circulation before we left the hospital and he gave us the all clear.

- Break between casts - Each cast should be on for 4-7 days, and there should be no break in between casts. This means that once the previous cast is removed there is 1-2-hour break before the next cast is applied. You should not remove the previous cast prior to your casting appointment; any increased amount of time out of the cast will lead to loss of correction that your cutie's foot has already made. If you doctor states that a break in casts is appropriate, make sure you ask lots of follow-up questions and do research to back up any decision you make. You can always get a second opinion as well.

- Skin issues - When a cast is removed there should not be major skin issues, such as blisters, scratches or abrasions from the cast. If skin issues occur there may an issue with cast application or tolerance, and you will want to discuss with your casting doctor on how to proceed with treatment. You can always get a second opinion as well.

- Cast removal questions - Different doctors may have different suggestions for cast removal, as some recommend soaking the cast and removing at home prior to the cast appointment, while others will remove the cast with a cast saw at the next cast appointment. Whatever way you and your doctor choose, make sure there is not a large window of time between cast removal and new cast being applied as there can be a loss of correction.

Our casting doctor removed the cast during the next cast appointment with a cast saw. While our cutie was not a fan of this process, and it was a bit frightening to witness as parents, we made this decision in case there was some reason that the next cast could not be applied the day we had planned. For example, if our doctor was out sick or there was a snowstorm that prevented us from getting to the hospital. We didn't want to risk taking the cast off and then not have the other one applied the same day.

- Any drainage from the cast - There should not be any drainage of any kind from your cutie's cast. If you notice any drainage, contact your doctor immediately for assistance.

- Foul smelling odor coming from the cast - If you notice a foul-smelling odor from your cutie's cast it might be an indication of a developing skin issue inside the cast. Please contact your doctor immediately if you notice any smells that are out of the ordinary for your child.

- Temperature of 101.3 or above - If your child develops a fever of 101.3 or above and has no other symptoms of a cold or infection, you will need to contact your casting doctor to ensure that there is not an issue with your child's casts.

- No lapse between cast and BnB - There should not be a break, even a day, between when your child's final cast is removed and when your child enters BnB. Any length of time can cause a loss of correction achieved throughout the casting treatment. If your doctor states that there should be a break for any reason, please follow up with questions and research you have found refuting this statement. You can always seek a second opinion at this time as well.

- Length of last cast following tenotomy - If you child has a tenotomy, their final cast will stay on longer in order to allow the heel cord to heal and lengthen properly. This cast should be on for 2-3 weeks total, depending on the recommendations of your casting doctor. It should be on for at least 2 weeks and no longer than 3 weeks. If your doctor suggests leaving the cast on longer due to a delay in getting the BnB, and the cast has been on for 3 weeks it is recommended that the cast be removed and a holding cast be placed on the foot until the BnB is ready and your cutie can make the transition.

- Tenotomy - Most clubfoot cuties will need a tenotomy in order to achieve the correct level of dorsiflexion to have a functioning and pain-free foot. There are cuties who will not need this procedure as their heel cord can achieve the flexibility needed without the procedure. This should be easy for your Ponseti trained doctor to determine based on the flexibility your child can achieve. If your doctor is on the fence about whether or not the tenotomy is needed this may be an indicator that your child will indeed need it.

  We had fellow clubfoot cuties who were told that they did not need a tenotomy, and after they transitioned to BnB, they realized that they did indeed need a tenotomy. We felt that if the tenotomy was even in question then we were going to do it because we did not want to delay any treatment for our cutie and wanted to give her the best possible chance at a smooth transition to BnB.

  Cuties who have not had a tenotomy but needed one, have a difficult time transitioning to BnB because their foot is not fully corrected.

Note: When I mention getting a second opinion, I realize that not everyone has access to an innumerable amount of Ponseti trained doctors in their area. In fact, we travel to another state for our cutie's treatment now, so I can empathize with the difficulties of finding a doctor you trust for a second opinion. If you are having questions about your child's treatment, there are doctors that you can reach out to via phone, email, or Facebook messenger to seek advice. They may not be able to give you their full medical opinion based on videos and photos. However, they should be able to help you decide whether or not you need to fully seek a different treatment path for your cutie.

Product recommendations:

- Permanent Markers - Sharpie Fine Tip 4ct - Target

  We used these to mark the toes in the cast and to decorate the casts!

- Receiving Blankets - Gerber Flannel 4pk - Target

We liked these to roll up and put under the casts to take pressure off the heels and provide support.

These are thin and soft and multipurpose, so can be used as a burp cloth and blanket in a pinch.

- Muslin Blankets - Aden & Anais Essentials 4pk - Target

We also liked these to put under the cast, they are longer and thinner than the receiving blankets and have the ability to be bunched up more underneath the casts if needed.

These can also be used for swaddles, nursing covers, car seat covers, and lightweight blankets.

- Bathwash - Cetaphil 2-in-1 Shampoo and Body wash- Target

This was our preferred body wash for our cutie. It was great for her sensitive skin when the casts were removed.

- Wash cloths - Softan Baby Washcloths- Amazon

We love these types of cloths because they are so soft and also become very soapy without having to use a ton of soap. Some cloths soak up the soap and you can feel like you are using a ton of soap, and they can also be rougher on the skin.

- Bouncy Chair - Fisher Price Baby's Bouncer - Amazon

We put our cutie in this all the time when we needed to do something without holding her.

It has the heels slightly elevated, which is great for supporting the casts and taking pressure off your cutie's hips and legs.

- Boppy Lounger - Target

A major staple for our cutie. We used it for just about everything, sleeping, holding, and hanging out. We would put our cutie in this and then place it on our older daughters' laps, so that they could hold her without worrying that the casts would be damaged. If you choose to have your cutie sleep in this, it is recommended that it be supervised sleeping.

Clothing

- Gerber Baby Organic Cotton 3pk Long Sleeve Onesies - Bodysuit with Mitten Cuff- Target

These are great because they have the mitt cuffs sewn into the onesie, which our cutie really needed because her hands were a major distraction for any resting or sleeping she was trying to do.

- Any onesie bought at Target, Amazon, Carters, or any baby retailer

Our cutie basically wore onesies and leg warmers throughout her casting. Since the cast goes all the way to hip the onesies work great and do not impact the cast.

- Gerber Baby Organic Cotton 2pk Long Sleeve Side Snap Shift with Mitten Cuffs - Target

We used these during casting appointments because they are easily removed without having to pull over the head (which our cutie hated). If the one she was wearing when the cast was applied got plaster on it, we could easily change her before making the trip home.

We also used these for sleep over the top of another short sleeve onesie for warmth and to keep her hands covered if they snuck out of the swaddle.

- Rompers- Burt's Bees Organic Baby Bubble Romper – Burt's Bees Website

If we wanted to change up the constant onesie, we would put her in one of these rompers which also did not impact the top of the casts. My mom bought us a couple of these when they were on sale and we really like them because they were cute and functional.

Leg Warmers

- Babyleggings.com - We bought most of our leggings from this website. We bought about 10 pairs and were given another 5-10 pairs of leggings from friends and family. These worked great and were large enough to fit over the casts easily. They were easily washed and had a large selection of designs.

You will want to order these prior to starting casting as they will need time to ship and arrive to you.

- JuDanzy.com - We were given a few pairs from this website and they worked fine for when she first started casting and the casts were smaller but were harder to fit on when towards the end when the casts got thicker.

    These can be purchased on Amazon as well, so they can arrive faster if you have 2-day shipping.

- Elena Miracle - Amazon

    We don't have direct experience with these but are another option offered through Amazon. Comes in a three pack

- Bow bear- Amazon

    Again, we don't have direct experience, but are another option provided by Amazon. Comes in a five pack.

Sleep Aids

- Embe Swaddle- 5-14 pounds - Amazon

    This product was simply a life saver! All my girls loved the swaddle when they were infants, and this provided the necessary stability to keep her in the swaddle with the added ability to have her legs out. (More about this product in the sleep section in Chapter 7.)

- Embe Transitional Swaddle- 12-18 pounds - Amazon

    We didn't have access to this product when our cutie was born, and wish we had because we would have used it. It is a newer product that also provides the ability to have the arms out and the legs out for transitioning out of the swaddle.

- Rock and Play - This product is no longer on the market, but you can search for a similar product that can be used for sleep. (More about this product in the sleep section in Chapter 7).

- Hiccapop Day Dreamer – Amazon

    We didn't have this exact product but something very similar that we used with our cutie when she was having reflux issues as it allowed her to be in a more upright position but also still have her casts supported.

Keep Going

The casting portion of clubfoot treatment can be stressful and exciting at the same time. It is amazing to see those little feet be transformed week by week simply from gentle manipulation of the feet and plaster casts, but if you run into an issue and need to adjust treatment in any way, it can be extremely stressful. Remember to trust your gut, if you think something is off and you see a red flag during treatment, contact a medical professional immediately. While we want to trust our cuties doctor to correct their feet, the reality is that not all doctors, or all clubfeet, are created equal and that might mean that you need to seek a second opinion. Be kind to yourself and remind yourself that you are doing everything in your power to ensure your cutie has the best possible care.

CHAPTER 2

TRANSITIONING TO BnB

IT IS YOUR BABY'S LAST week in casts, and you are getting ready for the transition to BnB. You have most likely done some research to prepare yourself and are feeling anxious and excited about this next phase of treatment. My husband and I were so happy to be finished with the casting phase, and the trauma of the tenotomy, that we were completely unprepared to transition to the BnB phase. We didn't think about questions to ask during the appointment with the doctor and physical therapist, nor were we emotionally prepared for the transition.

Discussed Topics:

- Prepping for Transition
- What is BnB?
- Last Cast Removal Appointment
- First Weeks of BnB Transition
- Important Tips when Starting BnB

Prepping for Transition

One of the reasons I felt unprepared for BnB is that from the moment I'd started researching treatment options I'd focused primarily on the castings. Basically, I'd completely ignored the BnB phase. While I was still pregnant with my daughter, I spent the majority of my research time focused on casting, choosing a doctor, and making sure that doctor was well-versed in the Ponseti method.

I don't want to minimize the importance of this research for clubfoot parents. I spent hours online learning about the negative outcomes for babies who were not treated correctly, and it scared me into awareness and action. But I didn't spend half as much time researching BnB informa-tion. After our cutie's final casts were removed, I felt as if the hardest part was over, and that we'd be heading into the "the maintenance phase" of her treatment. We were drastically unprepared for how much work the maintenance phase would require!

In hindsight, I believe the metaphor of a marathon is appropriate for the transition from casting to BnB. During the first few miles of the mara-thon (the casting phase), your doctor is the one running while you're on the sidelines. You're there supporting the doctor, making sure they have everything they need to succeed in those first few miles, but you're not actually running in the race. Then, the second phase of the marathon be-gins (BnB). Your doctor stops running, jogs over to the sidelines, and states unequivocally, "It's your turn to run." Wide-eyed you stare at them in total surprise. "What do you mean it's *my* turn to run?" you ask. Your doctor isn't giving up or quitting, as they will continue to be there to support you from the sidelines, but now it's time to switch roles.

You take a deep breath, clear your mind, and remember that you al-ready have everything you need to succeed. You have the right shoes, plenty of water, good athletic gear, a strong support system and most im-portantly, your will to succeed. I'm not going to lie; the first few miles are tough. Along the sidelines, your support system is cheering you on. When you feel like your legs may give out, all you have to do is glance at their supportive faces, listen to their cheers, and know they're with you until the finish.

Clubfoot treatment is a lot like this marathon; at least it has been for me. It is certainly not a quick fix; it is not one surgery and recovery and you are good to go. It requires you to put in daily work. You will not be 100% prepared for BnB transition, but you can equip yourself with the things you need at the beginning of the race to help make the journey as easy as possible. You have to remember that there is an end and while you won't always be able to see the finish line, you know it is there. But the only way to get there is to keep going — *no matter what keep going*. If you stumble or fall, remember, you have to keep going to get there. I promise you and your baby will make it. Just keep going.

What is BnB?

BnB is the acronym for Boots and Bar, which in clubfoot treatment refers to a boot on each of your cutie's feet with a bar connecting them. The function of the BnB is to maintain the correction that your cutie's feet achieved through casting and tenotomy. Your cutie will wear their BnB in various intervals of time (i.e. virtually all day to only at night and nap times) up until the age of four or five. Throughout this stage of treatment, you will continue to have follow-up appointments with your medical provider who performed the casting, but the responsibility for your child wearing the BnB falls solely on your shoulders.

Without the BnB, your cutie's feet will inevitably begin to lose their correction and will experience a relapse that will require further medical intervention and possible surgery to correct again. In fact, the BnB is so imperative to clubfoot treatment that the following stats are found in literature provided by Dr. Matthew Dobbs at the Dobbs Clubfoot Center at Paley Orthopedic and Spine Institute.

- About 90 percent of babies who stopped wearing the BnB as directed in the first year relapsed.

  o Second year - 70-80%

  o Third year - 30-40%

- A patient whose family does not comply with the protocol for the (clubfoot brace) is 183 times more likely to have a relapse than is one whose family complies.

With stats like that, you can understand just how important BnB wear is to clubfoot treatment. If your cutie does not wear their BnB as prescribed by your medical professional, the chances are that all the hard work you put in during the casting and tenotomy will be for naught. If you are anything like me, you will want to ensure that you do everything possible to help your cutie maintain their hard-earned correction and the best possible chance for pain-free feet as an adult. The best way to ensure this is through compliance with the BnB wear.

Later in this book, there is an entire chapter devoted to the boots, their accompanying bar, and all the other accessories you need to help you and your cutie succeed through BnB wear. But before we get there

here is a short explanation of what the BnB looks like and consists of. Here is a picture of our cutie's BnB on her very first day of BnB wear.

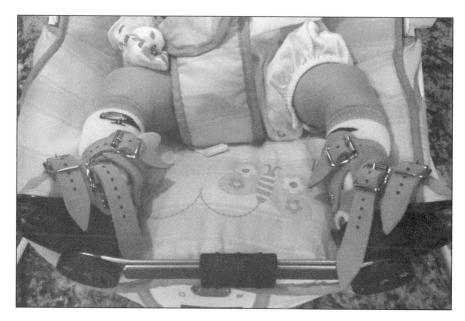

2.1 Our cutie the first day in BnB.

These Boots have leather straps with metal buckles and plastic bottoms where the bar clicks into place. This is the Ponseti bar that clips into the bottom of either foot. Even if your child has a unilateral clubfoot, they will be wearing boots on both of their feet, the only difference being the degree in which the foot is rotated. Our cutie's degree of rotation is 60 degrees on both feet. The degree for a corrected clubfoot should be 60-70 degrees, where a non-clubfoot would be set at 30-40 degrees. The buckles of the boot should be placed on the inside of the foot (as pictured above) as opposed to the outside of the foot. There are little heel windows on either side of each boot which will help you to determine whether or not your cutie's foot is placed correctly in the boot.

Last Cast Removal Appointment

The removal of the last cast is exciting because your cutie is finally done with those clunky casts and will have at least one hour a day with free feet. In fact, we were so excited to have the casts removed that we were completely unprepared for the beginning of the BnB. We didn't ask enough questions, and we spent the next couple of weeks floundering while trying to get our bearings. My husband says it was one of the most stressful weeks of his life, and he was taken off guard by how difficult the transition was. In the hopes that our experience will help you be more prepared for your own cutie's BnB appointment, here is a list of questions and suggestions that you might find useful.

First BnB Appointment Suggestions

- Measure the foot - Ask your doctor or nurse to take a measurement of your child's foot. Ask them to give you this measurement number (probably in centimeters). Some doctors take a measurement of the foot prior to the final cast in order to locate the correct boot size.

    o   Once you have that number, ask for the correct boot size to accommodate it.

    o   If you think the boot looks too small or big, ask for another size. Our doctor didn't take measurements as they have boots of all sizes in stock. If your doctor is the same, don't be afraid to ask to see how another boot fits if something seems off. This may be less of an issue if your cutie's foot was measured previously.

- Heel placement in the boot - Ask your doctor to show you exactly how much of the heel should be seen through the window. Take a picture of it for your reference at home. Also ask them when the boot needs to be readjusted. Have your doctor physically show you with the boot on your child rather than simply tell you.

- Ask when you should switch to a bigger boot, i.e. what signs to look for. Our doctor relayed that when the toes reach the end it is time to order new boots, and even if the toes even go over the edge a bit, it's still okay, this just means it's time to order. Have your doctor show you physically while the foot is in the boot what this looks like.

- Take pictures of what your child's foot should look like in the boot. Record heel window, toe placement, tongue placement, and whatever else you can think of, so you have it as a reference.

- Bar length - Ask when the length of the bar should be adjusted and how you do that at home. Take a video of your doctor showing you how to adjust the bar.

- Stretches - Ask your doctor to show you how to perform the stretches on your cutie and take a video that you can reference.

- Contact information - Ask whom to contact if you have questions or concerns and whom to contact in case of emergency. What is the best mode of contact, phone or email?

- Put the boots on your cutie before leaving the appointment - Even if your doctor has put on the BnB, ask if you can take them off and practice putting them on while they are there to assist you. This way you can ask any questions you have while putting the boots on.

- Degree - The bar has different degree settings. Have your doctor show you at which degree they should be set. Have them also show you how to adjust the degree if necessary. If you have a unilateral cutie the degree on each foot will be different with the non-clubfoot being set closer to 30 or 40 degrees. It is generally accepted that any setting between 60 and 70 degrees for the clubfoot is appropriate. If your doctor suggests a different setting, I recommend asking your doctor to confirm this, and if necessary, seek a second opinion.

It is good to have a healthy dose of nerves during this appointment. These nerves can propel you to ask more questions and take note of important tips and tricks. Take up the doctor's time. You are paying them for their services and moreover, this is their job! Don't feel the need to rush through the appointment to accommodate your doctor's schedule. This appointment is crucial for you to feel confident in transitioning your cutie into BnB. Had we taken more time during this initial BnB appointment; we may have had an easier go of it with our cutie.

First Weeks of BnB Transition

Your child has reached their last cast, and you know the transition to BnB is looming! We had mixed emotions. We were excited to be finished with the heavy, bulky casts, and so grateful to be past the tenotomy. My husband and I couldn't wait to get our hands on those little feet more often! At the same time, we were nervous about this next phase, as it meant we would now be in charge.

If you're anything like me, you like to have ample information and resources at your side before entering into something new. I had done copious amounts of research to ensure I knew as much as possible about this next stage. I wanted to be as prepared as I could be in hopes that it would make for a smoother transition.

I was recently listening to a podcast about clubfoot. This particular episode focused on preparing for treatment. The podcaster mentioned how powerless parents can feel at the initial diagnosis of clubfoot because there is nothing you can do but wait until your baby is born to start treatment. I remember feeling the same way, so I tried regaining my power by gathering as much knowledge as I could about clubfoot and its treatment. It helped while I was pregnant, but I had an "aha moment" during the podcast when I realized it is really the BnB phase of treatment when you, as a parent, get your power back. After all the waiting during pregnancy, and watching each cast be applied, and the tenotomy, you get to be in charge of your child's treatment.

But with this new-found power, there also comes great responsibility. You now are solely responsible for your child's care, and it is a big job. You are no longer standing on the sidelines of treatment watching and waiting for a chance to participate, you are in charge of their daily medical care. As the parent of a clubfoot cutie your responsibilities will include:

- Putting your cutie's boots on correctly.
- Following the structured wear schedule.
- Ensuring your cutie does not sleep without the BnB on.
- Checking the fit of each boot several times a day.
- Ensuring that the heel has not slipped up inside the boot and refitting the boot if it has.

- Checking the skin for any emergent issues, such as pressure sores or blisters.

- Performing stretches to help maintain flexibility three to five times a day.

- Ensuring the length of the bar between boots is the correct length.

- Ordering new boots when your cutie outgrows the old ones.

- Helping your cutie adjust to wearing the BnB by remaining calm and patient during what can be a difficult transition.

The first 2 weeks of BnB are the biggest learning curve. You have so much to learn and you largely have to do it on the fly. There isn't a training session to show you exactly how everything is done, so you and your cutie must learn as you go. It is not just a learning curve for you, but also for your cutie, who will have to adjust to not being able to move their feet independently. And finally, you have to find some semblance of routine. It can feel overwhelming and exhausting for everyone.

My husband is a very calm and collected guy. Stuff rarely fazes him (he lives with 4 girls remember?) but he said that it was the timing of it all that was the most overwhelming. For example, how were we to fit in the stretches and free time into our already packed schedule? The mornings were particularly difficult because we were so new at putting on the BnB and performing stretches that it took us at least twice as long as it does now that we are more experienced. So, in the midst of trying to get everyone else ready for the day we had to figure out how to incorporate at least 20 minutes of free time and 15 minutes of stretching. All of that coupled with our growing anxiety that we were not putting the BnB on right or performing the stretches correctly created an overwhelming environment. It certainly didn't help that our cutie took a few weeks to adjust to stretches and spent the whole time screaming her head off (more on this in Chapter 5 Stretching and Physical Therapy).

It was difficult to watch our cutie struggle and worry that we were the source of her discomfort because we were the ones putting the BnB on and were the ones performing the stretches. It took our cutie awhile to adjust to BnB schedule and to be honest I am not sure she ever truly adjusted during the 3 months of 23-hour wear, but we knew it was our responsibility to ensure that all the work we did during the casting phase was maintained to the best of our abilities. When you are feeling overwhelmed (which you will) and questioning yourself (I certainly did), remember that you can do this. Remind yourself that you have the power now. No matter how difficult the transition is, you have the power to keep moving forward.

As your cutie's primary treatment provider, it's crucial to listen to your instincts and trust your gut. If you feel that something is wrong, ask your doctor and keep checking back until you get the answers you need. For example, when our cutie first transitioned to BnB, we brought a pair of boots that another clubfoot mom had graciously given us at our first appointment. At the appointment, the doctor and his staff didn't measure her feet, and only visually checked her foot against the boot. We left the appointment feeling uncertain that these boots were the correct size. On our second day of BnB, I instinctively felt that the boots were too big. I called the nurse and drove to get a smaller size of boots two days later. I knew in my gut that something wasn't right.

While I was questioning myself during this time of transition and uncertainty, my husband urged me to follow my instincts, and I was glad I did. I can assure you that there will be moments during your cutie's clubfoot treatment, that if something feels wrong, it probably is. You need to trust your instincts. You are responsible for your child's care day in and day out now, so you know their feet best. When in doubt ask and research all possible situations.

We had *so many* questions during the first part of BnB, and we didn't know where to go for the answers. My mind would cycle through questions, and since I didn't know the answers there was never an end to the cycle. Here is a sample list of questions that we had and that you may ask yourself as well:

- Is her foot all the way back in the boot?

- Can I see enough of the heel through the heel window or has the heel slipped up?

- Is the boot tight enough?

- Is the boot not tight enough?

- Should I crisscross the straps of the boots to keep the heel in place?

- Should I use moleskin in the boot to help avoid blisters?

- Will the red marks on her heel ever go away or will they turn into blisters?

- How do I prevent blisters?

- Am I using the right type of sock? Is it too thick or too thin?

- Should I use the Foot Glide on her foot every time?

- When should I do the free time? How do I schedule the day to incorporate it?

- Am I doing the stretches right?

- How long should it take to do stretches?

- When should I do stretches? Before putting boots back on or right after they come off?

- How often should I do boot checks? (Remove the boot and replace to check the foot for skin issues)

- Who should I call if the red marks that appear do not go away?

- Is my baby uncomfortable?

- How do I comfort her when she is fussy?

- Is she fussy because she is an infant or because of the BnB?

- Is there anything I can do to help alleviate her discomfort?

These are just some of the questions we had, and because we didn't feel like we were getting the support that we needed from the current doctor to answer these questions, we inevitably made the decision to switch to a new doctor. It was a big decision but was what we needed in order to feel 100% confident in our cutie's treatment and I have never regretted that decision. It is my hope that you can use this guide as a resource to answer some of the questions that you might be having. But know that you should always be able to contact your medical professional if you are in doubt.

Important Tips When Starting BnB and Beyond

The following is a list of the most important tips and information about BnB wear and your cutie's journey ahead. The information below is referenced from the "A Parents Guide Through the Clubfoot Journey" from the Dobbs Clubfoot Center at Paley Orthopedic and Spine Institute (unless otherwise noted).

- There should not be any lag time from when the last cast is removed and you start BnB. It should happen in the same day. If it happens later than this, your cutie could lose some of the correction you have worked so hard to achieve. If your doctor suggests a gap of time between cast removal and BnB, you should get a second opinion or insist that this be completed on the same day.

- Bracing is a critical part of the clubfoot treatment. Clubfoot will relapse if the brace is not worn.

- The purpose of the BnB is to maintain the foot in the proper position, with the forefeet sitting apart and pointed upward. (www.ponseti.info)

- Both feet are put in the BnB even if your child has unilateral clubfoot, or one foot is affected.

- The brace should be worn for a minimum of 14 hours a day until your baby is fully walking, even if this carries them past the one-year mark.

- Be consistent. Have a routine that you can follow so that your child has an easier time adjusting to the brace.

- The brace should not hurt your baby but may take some time to adjust to.

  Personal note: I explain this like braces on your teeth. While they don't usually hurt, they take time to adjust to and are not exactly comfortable during the adjustment phase.

- Most babies take between two to seven days to adjust.

- Do not remove the brace if your baby cries, as this may make it more difficult to keep it on in the future.

    Personal note: We took off the BnB several times when our cutie was fussy and crying. While she usually calmed down after they were removed, when it came time to put the brace back on, we didn't hesitate and always stuck to our time schedule.

- The boots don't maintain your baby's correction without the bar. There is no point in your child wearing the boots if the bar is not attached. The bar is the corrective piece of the BnB and is what keeps the foot in the corrected position.

    Personal note: I have heard that some babies don't fit into the car seat with their BnB, therefore parents would leave the boots on but remove the bar for car trips. This should not be done consistently. We chose not to remove the BnB in the car seat, because our cutie spent a lot of time in the car and we wanted her to adjust to it. But this meant we had to buy a different car seat to accommodate her BnB.

- Do not stop using the BnB if you have problems. Clubfoot can recur without the bar. If you're having trouble go to your doctor or clinic and ask for help.

- The BnB cannot and will not correct the clubfoot, but it will keep the correction that was achieved through casting. If your medical professional suggests anything other than this, you should seek another opinion.

- If your child's foot is not fully corrected when entering the BnB phase, the BnB can be painful and your child's foot can slip out. If your child cries excessively and is inconsolable, or if their feet are slipping out of the boots, contact your doctor.

The following list is recommendations for helping your cutie adjust to BnB:

- Do not take the BnB off while the baby is crying. Wait until they have calmed down before doing so, therefore the baby does not associate crying hard enough with having their BnB removed. See more about this in the schedules section.

- The 23-hour wear is more about the baby getting/being used to the BnB rather than to maintain correction. Since your baby sleeps so much during this 3 month period, it is imperative that they always have their BnB on so that they adjust to the BnB more smoothly.

- You should expect your baby to be fussy while getting used to the BnB. Remember that the BnB is not painful, but it is new and different. Your baby can be easily frustrated while trying to adjust to the boots and bar, because they cannot move their feet independently. Remember that you and your cutie will adapt, just as you adapted to the casting phase. The first few weeks are always the biggest learning curve.

- You can play with your baby when the BnB is on. Move it around, straighten and bend it to help your baby learn how to move both feet together.

- It is vital that your baby learns to sleep in the BnB from day one. When you are struggling, remember that consistency in the beginning should beget easier wear for the next four to five continuous years.

The initial transition to BnB is most likely going to be the most confusing, overwhelming, and exhausting portion of the clubfoot correction journey. As with most things, it will get easier the more time you and your cutie have dealing with the complexities of the BnB. It was incredibly difficult to watch our cutie struggle to adjust to the BnB and try to manage our anxiety about our own ability to handle it all. Like us, you may deal with endless questions, minimal support, anxiety about skin issues, and sleepless nights, but it is vital that you don't give up. You have to remember all the hard work you and your cutie put in during those weeks of casting and that your end goal is to maintain that correction no matter what.

When I felt an overwhelming desire to give up and just take a break from the BnB, if only for just a few hours, I thought about how far we have come together and about how bright her future will be with pain-free, fully functioning feet. The moment my daughter was born the Beatles song "Blackbird" came to my mind and during her first casting appointment, I sang it to her as her doctor was applying the cast. It stayed with me as we struggled through the first few months of BnB and I would sing it to her in moments of strife in order to soothe her. My cutie is that blackbird who was born with broken wings and was waiting for the moment those fixed wings would help her learn to fly. It was my job to keep her wings in the best condition possible so when her moment comes, she will use them to fly anywhere her heart desires. It is your job to do the same for your cutie too, and you can do it, just keep calm and brace on.

CHAPTER 3

WORKING WITH DOCTORS

A S WITH ANY MEDICAL DIAGNOSIS, you will need to find the right doctor to provide the right treatment. Finding a doctor trained in the Ponseti method is vital to a successful treatment outcome. We also quickly learned that it was not just about a doctor who had the required experience but also one that we could trust. For us, trust meant a doctor who would take the time to answer any questions we had, give us detailed responses, and who offered us an ongoing engaged relationship that included open communication. To find this doctor, we had to make a difficult decision to switch doctors during treatment, and this chapter follows our journey through this process. I hope that it helps you if you are struggling with similar decisions or reaffirms that your current doctor is providing all the necessary support needed throughout clubfoot treatment.

This chapter also covers our experience working with our cutie's other doctors, such as her pediatrician, and our successes and failures in trying to advocate for her specific medical needs. The truth is that your cutie's medical needs will be different than those of a typical baby. At times, we felt unprepared to advocate for our cutie because of our inexperience. This chapter's goal is to learn from our experience and feel more prepared to navigate your cutie's medical treatment plan than we were.

Discussed Topics:

- Switching Doctors
- Variances in Treatment
- Pediatricians

Switching Doctors

We made the decision to switch doctors during our cutie's 23-hour BnB stage. One of the reasons I decided to write this book is also the main reason we switched doctors: we needed more resources and detailed answers to our questions. Our local doctor, who successfully completed our cutie's casting phase of treatment, was not readily accessible to answer our questions. And we had so many questions.

My husband and I felt like there was a lack of communication with our doctor during our cutie's casting phase. We would ask questions and not get the detailed answers we were hoping for. For example, we asked, "How are her feet progressing?" and our doctor responded with, "As I expect them to." This answer was unsatisfactory. Stating that our cutie's feet "looked good" to him didn't provide any concrete information about her progress. It was frustrating to feel as if we were not getting the reassurance we needed that her feet were being successfully corrected.

If you have done research about degrees of flexibility and levels of typical to complex clubfoot, you know that there are varying degrees of clubfoot. One of the most commonly used scales to rate the severity of a clubfoot is the clubfoot severity scale (Dimeglio Scale). This scale rates the foot from 0-20, with 0 being the least severe and 20 being the most severe (PGTCF p.122). Although we asked where our cutie's feet ranked on this scale, we were never given a straight answer from our casting doctor. Nor did the physical therapist who worked with our doctor tell us where our cutie fell on this scale. At one point I vaguely remember her saying that all feet were considered severe by their team or else they wouldn't require treatment, but we were never given an actual number to help us better understand the severity of her particular situation. It felt as if we were expected to blindly follow our doctor's recommendations, without any in-depth explanation on his part. He wanted us to trust him, without giving us the foundation of trust first.

Our doctor had a great bedside manner and was able to keep us calm during the casting appointments. We genuinely liked him as a person, but this made our visits feel more friendly and less professional. We often felt as if he was annoyed by our questions about our daughter's progress. We wanted concrete answers or explanations to questions we had about the flexibility of her feet, or her current dorsiflexion and whether or not a tenotomy would be needed to achieve the desired flexibility. Dorsiflexion is flexing the foot in an upward position. The movement at the ankle joint determines how far your child's foot can point upward (PGTCF p.18). There are varying degrees of dorsiflexion, in a non-clubfoot the degree of rotation can be up to 30 degrees, whereas the goal degree in a corrected clubfoot is 10-15 degrees. In a majority of cases a clubfoot child will need the tenotomy to achieve this goal.

None of this was explained by our casting doctor, in fact it wasn't until we met with a physical therapist at a different hospital location that we finally got real answers to our questions. The PT answered our questions about our cutie's current dorsiflexion and where it should be after the tenotomy. The simple fact that he sat down, with a physical model of a foot to show us what we were looking at, made us trust him more than we trusted our own doctor. He took the time to show us what her feet looked like now versus what they should look like post-tenotomy. His direct and detailed communication helped us understand so much more about our cutie's treatment. This physical therapist ended up being the person whom we turned to when we needed help with the transition to BnB, and he was the one we made an appointment with a week into BnB when we felt completely overwhelmed. We knew we could trust him to sit with us and take the time to answer our questions in a way that helped us understand without making us feel more overwhelmed.

Our casting doctor is a pediatric orthopedic surgical director who focuses on sports medicine, and also treated clubfoot. He saw his clubfoot patients one afternoon a week. He was trained under Ponseti and had experience with clubfoot, but like most doctors who treat clubfoot, this treatment comprised only a small portion of his practice. From the research I have done, it seems that most doctors who treat clubfoot do it as a portion of their overall practice. To me this meant that while our doctor was well trained in clubfoot treatment, he was not treating it all day every day.

I will always remember when we had our initial consultation with him before our daughter was born, I asked, "Have you ever had to refer to another doctor because a child's foot was too complex?" And his answer was a simple, "No." This was the only answer in the whole list of 100 questions I had for him that concerned me. I didn't understand how a doctor who only spends one afternoon a week treating a condition that could be complex in nature would never run into something that was outside of his scope. After reading so many posts in the social media groups about doctors who didn't correct the feet properly, I knew clubfoot treatment could be more complex in some cases. It made me question whether he would be unable to admit that he needed a second opinion because of his ego, rather than put the child's treatment first and refer out if needed. It made me second guess what would happen if our daughter's feet were more complex and he wouldn't refer us out. Unfortunately, this ended up being the case for two fellow cuties who were getting their casting treatment at the same time as we were. They were seeing the same doctor, and whether their feet were more complex or not, they both ended up switching to another doctor to redo a portion or all of the casting. Their experience did not help soothe my own anxiety and propelled us to get a second opinion and ultimately switch to another doctor.

I am so grateful to our casting doctor for correcting our cutie's clubfoot through the casting phase. I will never forget what he did for our daughter, and I do not look back at our experience with regret. However, we knew it was time to switch doctors when we transitioned to BnB due to the lack of communication and availability.

After having such a positive experience with our physical therapist, we knew it was time to find a doctor who would take the time to answer any questions that we might have. We made the decision to get a second opinion from Dr. Matthew Dobbs, a Pediatric Orthopaedic Surgeon, who was located at St. Louis Children's Hospital at the time (he has since moved to the Paley Orthopedic and Spine Institute in Florida). We made the decision to fly from Colorado to St. Louis based on all of the comprehensive research we had done on his expertise treating clubfoot. There were various recommendations on social media (there is even a closed Facebook group titled: Thank You Dr. Dobbs), our online research, his Linked-In Profile (my husband's type of research), and accounts of direct experience from fellow clubfoot moms.

Dr. Dobbs focuses directly on pediatric foot deformities. He has clubfoot clinics three times a week and performs surgery two days a week. He also does extensive research on ways to improve clubfoot treatment, and much of his practice is focused directly on clubfoot treatment. There was no question that I would trust his opinion of her feet. He trained with Dr. Ignacio Ponseti directly. His extensive experience treating clubfoot, combined with his continued research on the subject, solidified our decision to see him.

After meeting Dr. Dobbs and his team of medical professionals, we knew that we wouldn't be going back to our previous doctor. One of the most important reasons we decided to switch is the understanding Dr. Dobbs and his team have that clubfoot treatment requires an ongoing relationship between doctor and caregiver. Clubfoot treatment is not a one and done situation where you trust the surgeon to take care of your child during their surgical procedure. The treatment is ongoing for several years where things are ever-changing and there needs to be an open dialogue between parents and doctors about treatment.

When we had questions or concerns about her treatment, his team was immediately responsive. Even the literature Dr. Dobbs provided us about BnB, emphasized that if you are experiencing issues or have questions about the BnB, to contact them because, "you should not struggle alone." My husband and I were grateful that his team emphasized teamwork and encouraged asking questions throughout the entirety of the BnB phase. I have remained in constant contact with Dr. Dobbs and his team throughout the various stages of BnB wear and generally received a response to any question within 24 hours. It is the relationship that we have established that helps us continue to feel successful and confident in our cutie's BnB journey.

At the end of every follow-up appointment with Dr. Dobbs he always says, "You are doing a great job. Keep up the good work." This statement fuels me for the months between checkups because it affirms what clubfoot treatment really is. You as the caregiver are providing the daily treatment for your cutie and you are the one putting in the hard work to maintain the correction that your child has achieved. With this one statement, I knew that Dr. Dobbs understands the importance of our role as caregivers. He understands that while he may get a child's foot in the correct position, it is you, as their caregiver, who will keep it that way. By telling you that you are doing a great job, he acknowledges how hard this journey can be and simply how much work it is.

Traveling to see Dr. Dobbs is an inconvenience and costs more for our family, but his team does everything they can to assist with easing these burdens. Despite the inconvenience, it is worth the peace of mind to know that we are seeing a doctor whom we trust. At every appointment, he always takes the time to answer our questions and explains things in as much detail as we want.

I wanted to tell you about our journey of switching doctors because I think it is an important topic when talking about clubfoot treatment. I hope to affirm that it is okay to change your mind, even in the middle of treatment, about who is the best person to treat your child. If your instinct is telling you that something is off, or if you just aren't connecting with your current doctor, you can always seek a second opinion.

Yes, this may mean extra work, additional appointments and added costs, but this is a crucial time for your child's correction. I urge you to trust your gut. It is so important to find a doctor who is knowledgeable and experienced in the Ponseti method and one that you trust and can build an ongoing relationship with. Like I said at the beginning of this book, I had zero knowledge of what clubfoot was before my daughter was diagnosed, therefore I needed a doctor who could explain things, calm my nerves, and deliver the highest care possible. Take your time choosing the right doctor for you, do your research on websites, and even social media groups, and make the best and most informed decision for you and your child.

Maybe your casting experience was not ultimately successful, and you had to switch doctors to correct an issue that occurred. This happened to several of my fellow clubfoot parents. If this is your situation, please don't beat yourself up about choosing the "wrong" doctor. We all make the decisions we feel are the best for us and our cuties at the time. Now you have to be brave enough to make a new decision at this time and keep your sweet child's feet at the forefront of you mind. Know that you are making the best decision for your child and keep moving forwards, remembering that this journey is a marathon and not a sprint.

Or perhaps you are reading this book and you are second guessing your child's corrected foot, your doctor's ability to correct your child's foot, or your overall experience in general. Maybe you have told yourself that you have already come this far, and it would be too hard to switch. Or perhaps you feel terrified that something could be off, and you don't want to hear about it. I've been there. I spent many sleepless nights worried her feet were not fully corrected and we would have to repeat some, if not all, of the casting process. But I told myself that the only way I was going to quash my fear was to push forward and hear what the new doctor had to say. I couldn't let my fear stop me from moving forward, and you shouldn't either. If you have questions or concerns, get a second opinion. Stop thinking or worrying about it and do it. Make it happen now because the longer you wait the harder it is going to be to make the switch. You can do it! You are braver than you know and braver than you ever thought you could be. By God, you are a clubfoot parent now. You can do anything!

Variances in Treatment

It is important to note that there are variances in treatment between clubfoot doctors, just as with any doctor you or your child will see. My best friend and I frequently comment on how differently our pediatricians treat our kiddos. For instance, her pediatrician gives immunizations at 18 months and ours gives them at 15 months. Some pediatricians are reluctant to diagnose ear infections and others more willing to prescribe an antibiotic to treat it. While we often think of medicine as a science, there are variations in treatments and approaches from doctor to doctor. Medical diagnoses and treatments are simply not black and white.

Clubfoot treatment is no different. You may read on social media that your cutie's treatment differs in some way from another cutie's. While it is good to be aware and trust your instincts about your child's treatment, it doesn't necessarily mean that your child's doctor is doing something wrong. I've considered this a great deal while writing this book, because while my cutie has been treated a specific way, and her treatment has been successful to date, that *doesn't* mean another cutie's slightly different treatment will yield a less successful outcome. Yes, treatments may differ slightly from doctor to doctor, but that doesn't mean they are any more or less effective. Don't let yourself fall into the trap of comparison.

The Ponseti method outlines a detailed guide to treatment that should be followed by you and your doctor. If you think your doctor is not following the treatment guidelines, then you should seek a second opinion. However, if the treatment looks slightly different, but still has the major components of the Ponseti Method, then there may not be anything to worry about. I believe this is where having a doctor that you trust comes into play. You need to have a medical provider that you feel has your child's best interest at heart and will tell you if there is something different that needs to be done, even when it is difficult for you to hear.

A great example of the variances in clubfoot treatment is how doctors treat the decrease in hours of BnB wear. Several clubfoot parents who see different doctors were told slightly different things about how and when they should decrease their cutie's hours in the BnB. For example, one mom was told to go from the 3 months of 23-hour wear directly to

14-hour wear, whereas our doctor told us to move gradually from 23-hour to 18-hour then 16-hour and finally at the one-year mark 14-12 hour wear. Others have been told to go from 23-hour to 16-hour wear.

The decrease in hours is something that you are going to have to discuss with your own clubfoot doctor. I suggest doing some research of your own before discussing with your doctor so that you are prepared to ask any questions you may have about the plan. I remember asking our physical therapist why there was such a range of possibilities when decreasing hours, and he said that it was less about the chance of relapse and more about the baby being accustomed to the BnB long term. When we switched doctors, Dr. Dobbs said something similar. The decrease in hours is about your cutie's overall ability to cope in the BnB rather than the prevention of relapse. In the end, your cutie's ability to cope in the BnB will directly impact the overall success of treatment, so it is imperative. Be prepared to ask questions if you have them; your doctor is there to answer them. You will feel better if you ask your questions rather than continue to wonder and guess at the answers.

Our cutie's current doctor will not hesitate to tell us if something is off base and we need to alter her course of treatment. He doesn't care if these changes impact us negatively schedule-wise or may be difficult to hear. His number one priority is correcting her feet. He wants the absolute best for her feet regardless of what that means for her treatment plan, and to me that is what matters most.

Pediatricians

I love our pediatrician. So much so that I drive 30 minutes out of my way to see him. He opened his own practice after we started seeing him with our eldest daughter, and of course the new office wasn't right around the corner. He is worth the drive because he is the perfect balance of taking things seriously when warranted and helping me calm down when I am absurdly anxious. Once I was so worried that my eldest daughter wasn't getting enough breastmilk (nursing moms, you know what I'm talking about, right?) and he simply said, "Look at her. Does she look healthy?" I replied with a meek, "Yes" and he said "Well, then she is probably getting enough milk." He was effectively telling me to take a chill pill. It was exactly what I needed at that moment.

When our clubfoot cutie ended up in his office with symptoms of nothing more than a nasty cold, right before a scheduled trip to St. Louis for a follow-up clubfoot appointment, he tested her for RSV, because of my history of asthma. It turned out she had RSV, and we had to postpone the trip. I was so grateful that I did not try to power through a day trip with a baby who was actually very sick, and that was thanks to his diligence.

When I found out that our daughter would be born with clubfeet, I called him in the parking lot of our middle daughter's preschool while I was waiting to pick her up. Actually, I texted him (yes, another perk is that we're able to text him directly when needed) and he immediately called me. He reassured me that it would be okay, that clubfoot was something fixable and most of the time there are no other congenital complications. It felt mildly reassuring. Nothing could have reassured me fully at that point, but it was great to have this communication with him.

On that phone call our pediatrician briefly mentioned that clubfoot was surgically fixed. I soon figured out that this was not the case. It was in this moment that I realized I might end up more experienced than my pediatrician about my daughter's particular diagnosis, simply because I was going to live and breathe it every day. I subsequently found out that my cutie was our pediatrician's first clubfoot patient. There is a great chance that you will find yourself in a similar situation with your child's own pediatrician. It can feel overwhelming to know that you have more direct experience with a certain diagnosis than your child's primary care provider. But you can take heart in the fact that this will allow you to know what's truly best for your child and advocate for their care from that place of knowledge.

We would spend time discussing with our pediatrician and his staff about clubfoot treatment and its complexities. The BnB phase made us her main treatment providers, and our pediatrician and his staff would play an important supportive role with her clubfoot treatment, but we would be the leaders in her daily care. I hadn't experienced this with my older girls. Of course, I know my girls better than anyone else, but I was never their primary medical treatment provider. Sure, I gave them antibiotics when they were sick (no easy feat with my 6-year-old who detests medication like it's the devil), and I slept in their rooms when they coughed so hard they threw up, but in the end I followed our pediatrician's treatment plan because he was their doctor.

Clubfoot was different. I knew I had to trust my cutie's treating doctor during the casting phase, but after that I would be in charge of maintaining her correction. No one else was responsible for this crucial part of her care. Not her clubfoot doctor, not her pediatrician, but my husband and I alone. It wasn't "doctor knows best" anymore; instead it became "parents know best." My pediatrician still asks about her course of treatment at every appointment, and he even checked in on us when she had her tenotomy. He fully supported our decision to change doctors even when he thought our cutie's feet looked fully corrected. Yet, our pediatrician doesn't have more experience with our cutie's clubfoot treatment than we do. We have the opportunity to teach him something, and that experience will benefit him with his next cuties, because with odds of 1 in a 1000 he's bound to have another cutie come his way. When I asked him recently if he had any other clubfoot patients. He said he has had at least 4 since our daughter. You will have that same opportunity if you choose to see it that way. You can help your child's pediatrician gain experience in clubfoot treatment by simply sharing your experience with important medical issues that may be impacted.

Naturally there were moments of frustration when medical staff didn't seem to understand that having clubfoot made our cutie's "routine medical care" a bit more complicated. For example, when we took our daughter for her one-year well-child appointment and vaccinations, we forgot that she also had to have her hemoglobin and iron levels checked. With our older two girls this was mildly annoying because they had to prick their skin to get the blood drops, it took forever, and my babies screamed the entire time. But with our cutie, it was significantly worse because guess where they take the blood from? That's right, the danged heel.

First, I had already decided that I was going to let my cutie have a pass on her BnB in the car seat during nap due to the immunizations, but the heel prick compounded my decision. I was not going to put her heel into a boot immediately after she'd had blood squeezed out of it! I asked the nurse if the heel prick would impact my cutie's ability to wear her boots, and her response was an expected, "it shouldn't." But honestly, how can a nurse unfamiliar with clubfoot be expected to know about putting on double ply socks and strapping a baby's foot into a tight boot that allows for no flexibility? The answer is that she can't. She can't be expected to know about the experience of putting the BnB on your cutie, because she doesn't have direct experience like you do. During the course of this one-year doctor visit, my husband and I had to endure the nurse squeezing blood out of our cutie's heel for at least five minutes. I'm not exaggerating! It was five minutes of our cutie screaming and crying. We're obviously highly sensitive to anyone messing with her feet, because frankly, they've been through enough! Our cutie doesn't need anyone touching or tickling them, and definitely doesn't need blood squeezed out of them. While the nurse did her best, we still felt frustrated that what constitutes a routine procedure for one child might be considerably more complicated for a child with clubfoot.

When the nurse was finished, she told us that if any of the results came back abnormal, we would need to retest at 18 months. At this point we'd made the decision that if something appeared abnormal in the results, we would not retest unless absolutely necessary. We should have declined the test initially, since there were no signs of any issues and it wasn't 100% necessary. In hindsight, I believe I should have advocated for her more in this moment and asked our doctor if this test was absolutely necessary and what her outcomes might be if we chose to decline the test. Then I could have made a more informed choice without simply following a routine care plan for a typical child.

As clubfoot parents, we need to be prepared to have everything fully explained to us if it involves our cutie's feet. We need to ask questions. We need to remember that we are the most well-versed participants in our cutie's treatment, and as their parents we have every right to consent to or decline treatment as we see fit. If you have other children with no special medical needs, you probably haven't had to advocate on their behalf during doctor's visits; I know I didn't. Before we had our cutie, I rarely questioned our doctor because I was of the mentality that "the doctor knows best." I chose a pediatrician for my girls that I feel comfortable with and that I trust. Why would I question him unless absolutely necessary? Well, absolutely necessary happens quickly when you have a cutie, because you will most likely become more experienced than your child's pediatrician when it comes to clubfoot.

At this point it becomes imperative that you speak up when something feels off during a routine visit to your family doctor. The most important thing you can do as an advocate for your cutie is to ask questions and keep asking! Here are some questions that you might ask if your doctor suggests a treatment that doesn't sit well with you:

- Is this treatment medically necessary?

- Why does my child need this treatment?

- What might the outcomes be if we decline this treatment?

- What might happen if we postpone this treatment?

The same holds true for immunizations. If the timing of immunizations interferes with your cutie's clubfoot treatment, ask your doctor if it's possible to alter the immunization schedule. This is not to say I am anti-vaccination! To be clear, I am 100% pro-immunization and all three of my daughters are fully vaccinated, yearly flu shots included. What I am advocating is that you ask your doctor to explain why certain shots are needed at a specific time, and if you need to delay due to clubfoot treatment, what might that look like?

Our pediatrician was fantastic about allowing for flexibility in our cutie's immunizations. For the mandatory heel prick at 14 days, he met us in his office the day before her first cast went on, on a Sunday, to make sure we didn't have to hassle with it at the hospital before casting! He also delayed her two-month immunizations by a month, first because at eight weeks our cutie was still in full leg casts, and second because the shots were scheduled two days after she transitioned into BnB. Immediately after the removal of her final cast, we felt her legs needed a break and we needed time to help her transition to BnB without the added complications of potential immunization reactions. Our pediatrician completely understood and moved her appointment back 3 weeks to allow us time to adjust. By pushing back her two-month immunizations this also meant that it would push back her four-month and six-month immunizations because of the six to eight week waiting period between each round of shots.

I encourage you to advocate for what's best for your cutie. If your doctor downplays or refuses your requests, don't be afraid to ask them to explain their reasoning for their decision. Also, it is important to ask your doctor to chart *all* of their response to your requests and questions. If your doctor refuses your request to, for example, delay a heel-prick test, ask them to add both your request and their reason for refusal to your child's chart. If your doctor gives an unsatisfactory answer to one of your questions, ask them to chart this as well. Push yourself to go out of your comfort zone, even if it feels hard, when you look back you don't want to regret not asking the questions that you really needed answers to. Or maybe you are reading this and thinking, Well duh! Of course, I would ask our doctor the tough questions! I already do this! To you I would say, Awesome! Keep it up and take it a step further by encouraging your fellow moms to do the same, whether they have clubfoot cuties or not.

CHAPTER 4

MASTERING THE BOOTS & BAR

URING YOUR CUTIE'S BNB PHASE of treatment, you are guaranteed to become an expert on everything pertaining to boots and bar. But when your cutie is first transitioning, these weird looking boots with leather straps and metal buckles and their attaching bar can be daunting. How was I supposed to make sure my cutie was comfortable while wearing a brace connecting her feet 23 hours a day? I was going to have to figure out how to get these boots on correctly and ensure my cutie was able to adjust accordingly, which meant I was going to have to master these boots! During my cutie's first week of BnB, it took me forever to get her boots on and her heel in the right position in the boot. I honestly didn't know if I would ever get the hang of it, and that was just the boots. Then we had to figure out which bar was the right bar for our cutie, which inevitably changed during different phases of her treatment, and how and when we were supposed to adjust the length of the bar.

This chapter will hopefully serve as your go-to guide for all things boots and bar related.

Discussed Topics:

- Different boot types
- Detailed how-to instructions for getting the Mitchell Ponseti boot on
- Heel placement in the boot
- Where to purchase the boots and bar
- How to prep the new boots for maximum comfort
- The different bars available

- How to adjust the bar lengths
- Purchasing accessories for the BnB
  - o   Bar Covers
  - o   Socks
- Other items we purchased to help with BnB
- Where to buy walking shoes

Boots

There are different boot options available for clubfoot treatment, but the one that is the most widely used in the United States is the Mitchell Ponseti® boot. The original boot created was called the Markell boot. This boot is an open-toed and utilizes laces rather than straps and buckles to keep the foot securely in place. These are still used and available if needed; however I have not seen many families currently use these as they tend to favor the Mitchell Ponseti® boot.

The Mitchell Ponseti® boot can also be referred to as an AFO (ankle foot orthodic). This boot is a sandal-like shoe with three separate leather straps that cover the foot from ankle to toe. The goal is to keep the foot firmly but comfortably in place. As pictured in 4.1 and 4.2, this boot has a hard plastic sole, where the bar will be clipped in, soft rubber lining on the bottom of the foot and up the heel, with metal buckles for the straps. John Mitchell and Dr. Ponseti worked closely together to create this boot to provide the right balance of keeping the foot securely in place while maintaining comfort for the foot. The boot is designed to be worn "inside out," meaning that the metal buckles are on the inside of the foot rather than the outside. Since the Mitchell Ponseti® boot is the most widely used, and the boot that I have direct experience with my cutie, it will be what I refer to when I mention "boot" for the remainder of this chapter.

*4.1 Mitchell Ponseti® Standard AFO in Raspberry
(photo courtesy of MD Orthopaedics).*

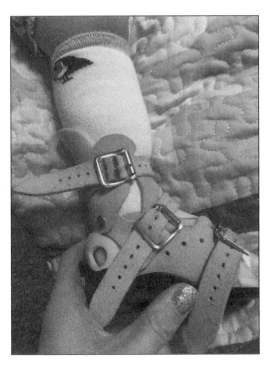

4.2 My cutie in her Mitchell Ponseti® AFO boot.

Purchasing the boots

Where you get your cuties' boots will largely depend on your medical professional and your health insurance coverage. Our casting doctor had boots of all sizes available at the hospital, so we were not required to order the boots prior to the transition to BnB. As you have read in Chapter 2, about our original issues with the size of the boots during our cutie's first week of BnB, you can also use a pair of used boots if you have some available from a fellow parent or through a Clubfoot Exchange Program such as the one found on the Clubfoot C.A.R.E.S. website (https://www.clubfootcares.org/clubfoot-boot-exchange-usa). Just keep in mind that if you are planning to use a program such as this for your cuties first pair of boots, you will need to order ahead of time to ensure there is no delay between when the final cast is removed and when you child begins their BnB wear. The exchange boots can take up to 4 weeks to arrive. This program is also a great place to donate your cutie's used boots when you are done with them!

Another option when purchasing the boots is to order them directly through MD Orthopaedics. This company was founded by and run by the man who created the Mitchell Ponseti® boot, John Mitchell himself. I seriously love this company because not only did John create an amazing product for clubfoot cuties around the world, but the customer service is exceptional. When we realized that going through our health insurance to purchase the boots was more expensive (double the amount) than purchasing the boots directly through MD Orthopaedics, we simply cut out the middleman and have never looked back. There is no delay in getting the boots as they are shipped the same day if the order is placed on a Monday-Thursday before 10:00 a.m., and they ship for free! The company does everything possible to make the boots cost effective for families. (https://mdorthopaedics.easyorder.com/easyorder/index)

When ordering new boots, you will want to make sure that you have the correct measurement of your cutie's foot to make sure you are getting the right size. You should work with your medical professional to ensure you have the right measurements, but if you need new boots and you do not have the ability to consult your child's doctor, there is a guide on MD Orthopaedics website that can help you determine the correct size (https://www.mdorthopaedics.com). Since we have quarterly checkups with our cutie's doctor, we usually discuss with the Orthotics specialist the anticipated time frame for ordering the next size.

How to Put on the Mitchell Ponseti® boot

1. *Check the visual: If you have ordered through MD Orthopedics, you will receive a visual with the order. This has pictures and explanations on about how to get the foot correctly placed in the boot.*

4.3 Image of fully buckled Mitchell Ponseti® AFO
(all illustrated images courtesy of MD Orthopaedics)

2. *Start with the Middle Strap: We like to start with the middle strap, move to the top strap, and finish with the toe strap. We usually put the middle strap as tight as we want it and then move on. You can also get the middle strap snug and then move to the other two straps to tighten and then go back and make sure the middle strap is tightened enough.*

    - The middle strap is the most important strap. It keeps the heel down and the foot in place more than anything else. You want to make sure that this is your focus when putting the boot on. You also want this strap to be the tightest strap.

- The other two straps can be loose. Loose enough that you can push the top of your finger under but not so loose that your finger easily fits under.

- The middle strap should be tight enough that you cannot fit your finger under it at all. The middle strap will also naturally feel tighter because of the tongue of the boot. The tongue relieves the pressure from the snugness of the strap but it can also add bulk, which can make it seem too tight when it really isn't.

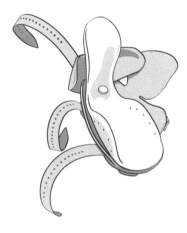

4.4 Open AFO boot before the foot is placed inside, buckles on the inside of the ankle.

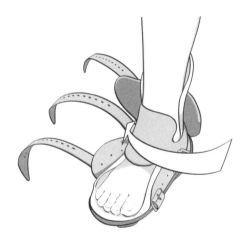

4.4a Pull the tongue across the middle of the foot and hold in place while buckling the middle strap.

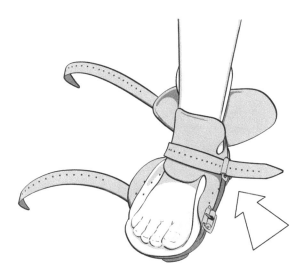

4.4b While holding tongue placement, secure the middle strap first.

3. *Buckles on the inside: The buckles of the shoe should be on the inside of the boot as it keeps the foot in place. It is the opposite of most normal shoes where the buckles are on the outside.*

4. *Mark the Straps: Once you have a good fit and the straps are the correct tightness, you can mark the appropriate hole so that there is less guessing. This can be especially important if someone else is putting the boots on for your child. We used a permanent marker to mark the boots. As the leather of the straps loosen you may have to adjust your spot tighter or if your child's foot grows and you are waiting for new boots you may need to loosen the strap if it is causing discomfort. Remember, the mark becomes a guide but not a rule.*

   - For us, the middle strap usually stayed its course for the entirety of the wear of the boot, but the top and toe strap adjusted tighter as the leather loosened up.

4.4c Buckle the top, ankle strap, and the bottom, toe, strap to complete.

5. Heel window: This tiny window can cause a great deal of stress, but it also can be a great way to check the fit of the boot. When you first transition to the BnB, there is a lot of talk about how far down the heel should be in the window. How much of the heel should be visible through the window? This was one area that we received lots of information about and some of it seemed conflicting. I have attempted to consolidate the most pertinent and accurate information regarding the heel window below. See pic 4.5 for reference.

4.5 The heel window of the AFO, where you can check the placement of the heel inside the boot.

- You should be able to see 75% of the heel through the window.
  - o It takes 2-3 weeks for your baby's heel to drop to fit into that window.
  - o The heel will not fit completely flush against the boot until your cutie starts walking and bearing weight on their heels. The gravity is what makes the heel completely drop.
  - o Each boot size up has a deeper heel pocket and your baby will take a little time to adjust to the new fit.
  - o The tighter the middle strap, the more of the heel you should be able to see.
  - o You need to refit the boot if you cannot see the heel at all.
  - o The heel should not remain completely out of the window consistently because it can cause skin issues with the foot.
  - o The window was originally designed by Dr. Ponseti to relieve pressure and increase comfort for the heel of the baby, not as a gauge for whether the foot was in place or not.
  - o If the heel is consistently slipping out, the boot may be too big, and you may want to size down.
  - o If the heel still is consistently coming up and will not stay in place, it may be an indicator that the ankle is not reaching the necessary amount of flexibility.
  - o If your baby can slip out of the boots at a young age, the boots are not fitting properly.
- This can also mean that the foot is not fully corrected and may need another tenotomy.

  Dr. Dobbs states that most parents have problems in the first several weeks of BnB because they try to shove the foot back in the boot in order to see the heel through the window. This can end up hurting the foot. Dr. Dobbs recommends making sure that the middle strap is tight, stating that the heel will eventually drop, and it will show through the window.

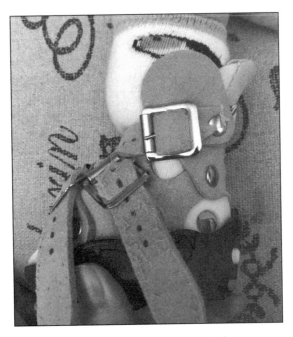

4.5a My cutie's heel window during 23-hour wear.

4.5b My cutie's heel window during 14-hour wear.

During our cutie's first few weeks in BnB, we spent a lot of time worrying that her foot was not in the boot correctly. I have very small fingers and my pinky finger is especially small. At night I would put my pinkie in the heel window to feel if her heel was down. This wasn't always a foolproof method but worked much of the time. If I couldn't feel her heel, or I could just barely feel it, we would readjust her boot. Sometimes it was a false alarm, especially as she got older. The heel would be settled back into the boot and when I would feel on one side of the boot it would make me think her heel was up and when really it was just back further in the boot.

I liked the "pinky method" because it seemed the least disturbing way to check her heel placement. Our cutie was already a terrible sleeper, and I wasn't going to exacerbate it by turning on the light to check her heel unless absolutely necessary! We even went as far as using the flashlights on our phones to readjust the boots rather than turning the full light on at night. Of course, this skill wasn't immediate, and we had to use the full, bright light in the beginning. It was easy for me to check my cutie's heels while I was nursing her in the middle of the night and my husband could check when there was a diaper change needed.

Personal note: My husband and I have very different, and I like to think complementary, personalities when it comes to how we approached this part of the treatment. He is much calmer and less vigilant than I am. I am more anxious and tend to overreact, which leads me to be more vigilant. There were times when he would say our cutie's heel looked fine and I would look at it and thought her boot should be readjusted. I was hyper aware, and he was calmer, which I believe led to a healthy balance when it came to the BnB.

During the first few weeks of BnB, my husband and I realized that putting on her boots would be a two-person job. We would each take one foot and put that boot on. This made the process faster and helped us avoid an extended crying fit. But as our cutie got older, we had to stop splitting up because it was harder to get the boot on straight from a side position. My husband eventually told me to stop trying to help because it was only making it harder to get her foot in the right place. I learned my lesson one night when our cutie was especially cranky at bedtime and I insisted on helping. Later that night, I noticed her heel on the foot that I'd "helped with" had slipped up, and we had to redo it.

After that experience we decided that one parent would be in charge of putting on both boots and the other parent would be responsible for creating distractions. As our daughter grew, she became squirmier and less patient as we put on her boots. So, it made sense for one parent to focus solely on this job. For both of us, it was much easier putting her boots on while she was lying down. As our cutie got older, she would try to sit up as we were putting her boots on! She wanted to move and certainly didn't want to lie still for any period of time. We especially wanted her lying down as we tightened the middle strap, so the "distraction person" became even more important during that time. It was still a two-person job, but the roles had evolved.

Here are some distraction strategies that worked for us:

- Sing nursery rhymes - Our cutie's favorites were "The Itsy Bitsy Spider," "Twinkle Twinkle Little Star," "The ABC Song," and anything by The Wiggles.

- Read books - Our cutie particularly liked short board books that could be read again and again.

- Easy to grasp toys - Small toys that she could move from hand to hand easily were a good distraction.

- Noise makers - Rattles, toy keys, or other small noise-making toys are great for distracting your cutie.

When You Get New Boots

Your cuties will transition to new boots when they outgrow their current boots. It wasn't intuitive to know exactly when our cutie was ready to move up to the next size of boot. Our casting doctor told us that the width of the shoe was more important than the length. Meaning, even if the toes were hanging off the edge, as long as the sides of the shoe were not digging into the foot, the boot was not too small.

In our experience, recognizing it was time for the next size of boot was not nearly this clear-cut. There wasn't a moment when we looked down and thought "it's time for new boots!" It generally sounded more like my husband and I asking, "Do the boots seem too tight?" several times over the span of a couple of weeks before me made the decision to order new boots. Or, I waited until our follow up appointments and asked the orthopedist.

It is important to order your cutie's next pair of boots before you think that they will need them. There can be a delay in receiving the boots, especially if you are ordering them through your doctor or insurance. We didn't experience a delay when ordering directly from MD Orthopaedics, but there was a delay when we ordered boots through our out-of-state doctor. We figured it was better to have the new boots on hand so that we could wash and prep them as necessary before it was time to transition.

By our cuties' one-year mark she had been through 000, 00, 0, 1, and 2 size boots. There didn't seem to be a big difference in transitioning her through the smaller, zero-sized boots. But as she transitioned into the larger sizes the boots seemed to feel stiffer as we got them. Our doctor confirmed this suspicion during one appointment, stating that as the boots moved up in size the stiffness increased and were less flexible. He also stated that is better for the boot to be snug than too big. This meant we had to adjust the transition process accordingly. The nice part about the need to have a longer adjustment time to the bigger boots is that you have the smaller boots already, so you can switch between them. When you get your first set of boots, and your cutie has to wear them 23 hours a day, there isn't much wiggle room to adjust. That part gets easier as your cutie gets older.

Washing Boots

To soften the leather and make the transition easier, we washed the new boots at least once before starting the transition. Here is the method that worked best for us:

- Place boots in a mesh laundry bag.
- Put in two or three towels surrounding the bag.
- Do not add soap.
- Gentle cycle.
- Warm water.
- Let them air dry for 24 hours.
- Place them in a sunny spot if you want them to dry faster

I'll admit that the first time I put the boots in the washer, I felt nervous that I was going to damage them in some way, and those babies are expensive! Not only are they costly, but necessary for her to wear! If something happened and I had to reorder boots it would cost time and money. This is yet another reason to order boots in the next size up, in case something happens, and you need an extra pair.

This is especially true in the early stages of 23-hour wear. During this period, you don't have time to spare like you do in night/nap wear schedule. Despite my anxiety about washing the boots, they always came out fine. During the summer months I would put them outside in the sunlight to help them dry more quickly, and in the winter months I would put them on a windowsill that received the most direct sunlight. The boots would be completely dry within 24 hours.

I recommend using the Laundry Mesh Bags (from Amazon). They come in a 6 pack. We use these to keep all our cutie's socks for the BnB together when we wash them. I put all the dirty socks in one bag and then throw that bag in with all the other dirty clothes. This also makes it easier to grab the bag out of the clean clothes in the washer so that I don't accidentally dry the Black Robin socks.

- Using the bag made finding and sorting the socks 100 times easier. I would recommend it to anyone who has many socks to wash.

- I also used these bags when I washed the AFO boots prior to our daughter wearing them. I would place both boots in the bag before putting them into the washer.

When my cutie moved from size 1 to size 2 boots, we made the transition much slower--a two- to three-week process--because she seemed to have a harder time adjusting to sleeping in them. We had to remember that it was going to take longer for her to break the boots in now that she was in the 12-14-hour wear phase, simply because she wasn't in them as much. I also think that the size 1 boot was too small, but the size 2 boot was too big, and she really needed an in-between size, but since those don't exist, we adjusted our transition schedule accordingly. We started with her naps, which meant only an hour or an hour and a half of wear. Then we added the boots to the second nap, so she was in them for a total of 3-4 hours a day.

We also washed these boots twice, since we were transitioning more slowly and had the time to allow them to dry. The first time our cutie wore them overnight, she woke up screaming at an unusual time for her. When we checked the boots, we noticed that one heel had come up, and we switched her back to the smaller boot for the remainder for the night. We waited another week before we tried the larger boots overnight again. We were able to do a slower transition due to the fact that she had not completely outgrown her current boots. She was not in dire need of new boots, as she wasn't busting out of her current ones.

We had a previous experience when ordering boots where there was almost a month delay in getting them and we needed to transition her immediately, so we didn't have the luxury of a slow transition. This is another reason to order boots before you think you need them. From size 1 to size 2 it probably took us a full month before she was wearing them full time, for both night and nap. Through the slow transition, we were able to avoid any red marks or blisters on her feet, and a smoother transition overall.

Quick Tip Reference Guide

There is so much to remember when dealing with the boots and bar, here is a simple list of quick tips to keep in mind when managing the boots:

- Order new boots as soon as you think the current ones are getting snug.
- Wash new boots before wearing (maybe even twice).
- Use the mesh laundry bags to wash the boots (and socks).
- Transition slowly, start with new boots at nap.
- Move toward overnight wear, but back off if your cutie is having a difficult time adjusting.

ADM Boots: Abduction Dorsiflexion Mechanism

This is another boot option that does not have an attaching bar, as it is a stand-alone boot. It was created to assist with abducting and dorsiflexing the foot, using two springs which are anatomically aligned to sub-tala and tibiotalar joints thus allowing normal, natural movement of the foot.

When ADM springs are working, they hold a low intensity stretch when the wearer is resting (https://c-prodirect.com/Content/Images/uploaded/ADM%20Downloads/casestudies/127_MKT_JDB_v001.pdf).

We chose not to use this boot option as there was not enough research to prove that it was an effective form of treatment. This is not to say that this treatment isn't effective for some people, but for us, the risk of relapse was enough to keep us on a course of treatment that we knew had the best chance at helping our cutie avoid a relapse. I'm sure there are successful cases of treatment using the ADM and have seen multiple parent testimonials on social media relaying their cutie's successful treatment with the ADM boot. Neither our casting doctor nor our BnB doctor recommended the ADM for use with our cutie.

As we do not have direct experience with the ADM, I will not elaborate on how to use them or where to find these boots. If you are interested in using the ADM, I suggest you discuss this treatment option with your doctor.

Different Types of Bars

There are two primary types of bars: the Ponseti Bar and the Dobbs Bar.

Important tips about what every bar should have:

- Adjustable fit widthwise - You shouldn't have to replace the bar often.

- Quick-release style bars; shoes snap on and off - This makes it easy to get your child in and out of the BnB. The bar holds the feet in the correct position: It does this by keeping the correct degree of the foot at usually 60-70 degrees on a corrected foot and 30-40 degrees on a non-clubfoot, if it was a unilateral clubfoot diagnosis.

Ponseti Bar

This bar was designed by Dr. Ponseti for clubfoot treatment. Pictured in photo 4.4, it is stationary and adjustable width-wise, but does not have the articulating portion of the feet. We started with the Ponseti bar when our cutie transitioned to BnB, since this was the only bar our doctor recommended and had available. We never had any issues with this bar and never had to adjust the width since our cutie was only in it for four months. The bar isn't very thick which made it easy to fit for bar covers. We continued to use this bar until our daughter was six months old, at which time we switched to the Dobbs articulating bar.

4.6 Photo of Ponseti Bar.

Dobbs Bar

Dr. Dobbs created a bar that keeps the feet in the same degree as the Ponseti bar but allows each foot to articulate independently. The Dobbs bar also has a stationary bar that can be used for babies under six months. The articulating Dobbs bar, pictured in 4.7, is only recommended if your cutie is six months or older. After the six-month mark, there are two bar sizes. The small size lasts until the one-year mark and the regular size lasts for the remainder of BnB wear, until four/five years old. You need to switch your cutie from the small size to regular size because as your baby grows bigger, they get stronger. The springs in the articulating part of the bar are looser on the small bar and stronger on the regular bar.

When you switch to the regular bar, or make any adjustment to the bars (including the width), it is recommended that you do it when you are not also switching sizes of boot. Whenever you are making a switch it is good to do it one at a time so as not to overwhelm your cutie with too much change at once. You want to make every adjustment as comfortable as possible for your cutie, and even slight adjustments to the BnB can have an impact.

We ordered both Dobbs bars from MD Orthopeadics. The regular bar came unassembled and we had to assemble it. We adjusted the regular bar width once. This was done at a doctor's appointment, in the first 12 months. I was confused about where to measure with her shoulders and didn't realize the measurement should be based on the outside of your baby's shoulders, not on the inside. Honestly, it's hard to tell when the bar is not wide enough. If you are in doubt, ask a trusted medical professional. Your doctor, physical therapist, or a nurse should be able to tell you if the bar is the correct width either in-person or based on photos you send them.

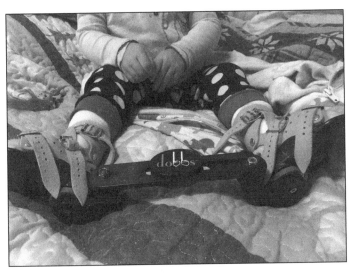

4.7 My cutie in the Dobbs bar.

Adjusting the Length of the Bar

If your cutie is having trouble adjusting to the BNB, you can try widening the bar a little, as other parents have mentioned that it helped their baby adjust to have a slightly longer width of bar.

Ponseti Bar:

1. Remove the bar cover.

2. Use an Allen wrench on the middle of the bar to slightly loosen the screw

3. Slightly pull the bar to increase the length and retighten the screw when the correct length is achieved.

4.8 Ponseti bar length adjustment image.

Dobbs Bar:

1. Remove the bar cover.

2. Find the two screws on the backside of the bar.

3. Use a Phillips head screwdriver to loosen each screw.

   Loosen enough to adjust the bar but not all the way so you don't have to completely reassemble the bar.

4. Adjust the length of the bar so that the middle screw on the snap of each boot is on the outside of your cutie's shoulder.

5. Once it is adjusted correctly, tighten the middle screws and replace the bar cover.

You may notice that you can also adjust the degree setting on the bar as well. As mentioned in Chapter 2, the degree should be set by your doctor at the first BnB appointment, and it is not recommended that you adjust it at home without consulting your doctor first. We personally have never adjusted the degree on either the Ponseti bar or the Dobbs bar. I have heard that some cuties do better with differing degrees if they are really struggling with the transition to the BnB, but I would not recommend making any adjustments without consulting your doctor first.

A fellow clubfoot mom friend experienced the degree disk on the Dobbs bar move over time; her cutie was originally set at 60 degrees and it had moved closer to 70 degrees. When she contacted her doctor about this, they mentioned that this can happen and sometimes the disk needs to be replaced in order to keep this from happening. I recommend checking the degree occasionally and then contacting your doctor if you notice any difference. I personally think that the degree on the Dobbs bar is more difficult to read because it uses lines rather than dots to indicate the degree setting, but I wouldn't give up the articulation of the Dobbs bar for this reason. The Dobbs bar degree setting is on the line below the number, so if set at 60 the number will be above the line. Another mom said that her cutie stayed with the Dobbs static bar rather than switching to the articulating bar because when they tried to transition the bars her cutie's sleep went downhill and the doctor told her not to mess with success.

4.9 Image of degree settings on right side of the Ponseti Bar

Another clubfoot parent mentioned that her son had difficulty transitioning to BnB. She researched another bar and asked to switch their son from the Ponseti Bar to the Dobbs Bar. Their cutie adjusted much better with the Dobbs bar. It is always good to know your options so that you can adjust when necessary. This friend said that their doctor did not offer the Dobbs Bar as a treatment option and they had to specifically request it. Know the differences in the bars, and don't be afraid to ask for a change if you think it will help your cutie.

While it may feel like you should be able to figure this all out on your own, it isn't exactly instinctual. It wasn't first nature for me, and it led to a lot of second guessing myself. When in doubt, ask someone you trust. Personally, I did not go on social media groups to ask questions like this because it felt too public and I wanted information from people I knew personally. I had read a fair amount of misinformation on social media pages and wanted to make sure that I was getting accurate information from a trusted source. You might feel differently, but always consider the source of the information before you make a decision that could alter your cutie's course of treatment

When our cutie moved to the final articulating Dobbs bar at 14 months, I was surprised by how squeaky it was. I would never have noticed, since at this point, we were not sharing the same room at home, but we shared a room with our cutie when we went on a family vacation. I could hear the bar squeaking all night when she was rolling around in her crib. I thought maybe something was wrong with the bar, so I asked my other clubfoot mommas and they said they were experiencing the same thing. One mom said they put vegetable oil on the hinges of the bar, where the noise was coming from and it seemed to help. This shouldn't be an issue with the stationary bars because they don't have the hinges.

Bar Covers

One of the most helpful accessories when starting BnB is a bar cover. This item provides padding for the middle of the bar, between the boots, and is usually made of padded fabric with snaps to wrap around the bar. These are great to have because it will provide protection for everything that your cutie's BnB comes in contact with, the carseat, stroller, crib, high-chair, or your lap! Like any good accessory, it also provides some aesthetic pleasure as well! They are cute to look at and a fun way to celebrate your cutie's individuality during the BnB wear. As my cutie now says, "It's cute!" When she gets older, I look forward to having her pick out a cover that she loves. There are several places that you can purchase a bar cover, below is a list of places that I have purchased from and my experience with them, as well as options for making your own.

I have purchased many bar covers for my cutie from 26th Avenue Bar Covers (Pictured below in 4.10). I have never had a bad experience when ordering through them. If there was ever an issue with a fabric I chose, such as it was no longer available, the business owner contacted me immediately and gave alternative suggestions. Each cover has two fabrics, so it is reversible. I bought a lot of holiday prints for Halloween, Thanksgiving, and Christmas that were super cute. A fellow clubfoot mom referred me here after our cuties entered BnB, and she said she even sent some fabric she had chosen to them and they used that fabric to make the bar covers.

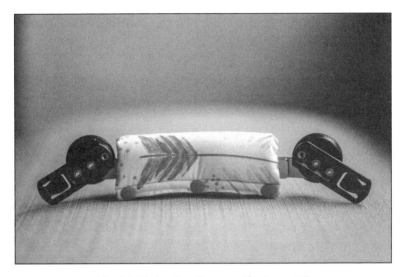

4.10a A 26th Ave Bar Cover on the Ponseti Bar.

Here is a list of places you can get bar covers:
26th Avenue Bar Covers- Direct Website, Facebook, Instagram (https://26thaveclubfootessentials.com; facebook.com/26thaveclubfootbarcovers; #26thaveclubfootessentials)

- Fast turn around
- Easy online ordering through Facebook
- Customizable with name and tags
- Lots of different fabrics
- Holiday/Special Occasion
- Buy 4- get 5th free
- Width and foam thickness customizable too

- Offers a program to help families who need financial assistance, as well as a donation program.

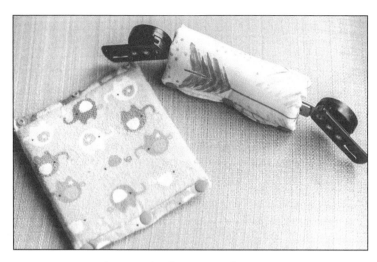

4.10b A couple of our covers from 26th Ave

- Etsy
  - o I bought one bar cover on Etsy. I was hoping to have it in time for our cutie when she first entered into BnB, but it was delayed, and it didn't arrive in time.
  - o The quality of the cover was great, and it actually fit a bit better than the covers I ordered from 26th Avenue, but that was probably because I didn't measure the length of the bar before ordering.

*I ended up not ordering through an Etsy vendor again simply because of my great experience with 26th Avenue Bar Covers.

- Baby Bumblebee Shop (Etsy shop) - Recommended by clubhub (https://www.etsy.com/shop/BabyBumbleBeeShop)

You can also make your own bar cover:

- Use pool noodles - some people buy a pool noodle and cut it down to the right size, then cut it lengthwise and slide the bar inside of it. I almost did this because our cover didn't come in time but ended up using a cover given to us from another mom.

Note: Pool noodles can be difficult to find if it's not pool-season, but ordering through Amazon is always an option.

- Sew your own pattern: I talked with many friends who either sewed their own bar covers or had family members sew special ones for their cuties. This is not my forte, and I knew I wouldn't be able to come up with something nearly as nice as the covers I bought! But if sewing is a strength of yours, I say go for it. How special would it be to make something for your child that they can keep for years to come? It sounds amazing to me!

Here are some quick tips to keep in mind when purchasing bar covers:

- I liked the double foam rather than the thinner. I felt it added more protection and fit the bar better.

- The width of the cover should match the width of the bar; however, it is better to be too short than too long because it is hard to squeeze on if it's longer than the bar.

- It's a good idea to measure the length of cover you'll need. We didn't measure and our initial batch from 26th Avenue were too short.

- I recommend getting multiple covers for the three months of 23-hour wear. This is when the covers will get the most use and be most visible.

- I bought five covers for 23-hour wear, five more for holidays and 18-hour wear, and just one nice one for 14-16 hour wear, because it was mainly worn during night and nap.

- If you choose to get your child's name on the bar cover, it makes it easy to check if the bar is the correct way. I used this trick when someone else was putting on our cutie's BnB on before nap. It was easy to say, "you know the bar is the right way as long as you can read her name correctly."

Socks

What I've come to discover is that there is a lot of variety in the socks that fellow clubfoot parents use for their cuties. What works for one child may not work for your cutie. Be patient, as it might take some trial and error to find out the best option for your cutie's feet. I will share what worked for us, but you can research other options on clubfoot websites and even ask your doctor what they recommend. I did ask our casting doctor what socks I should purchase in preparation for BnB and his response was, "whatever she looks cute in." Well this answer was obviously *not* helpful and frankly annoying! This left me to figure out what socks worked for us without any help from him.

To wash the socks, turn them inside out, place in a mesh laundry bag (easier to find all in one place), wash with other clothes, take out of washer and lay flat to dry (drying these socks in the dryer can cause them to shrink.) I stretch each sock out while they are wet and before I lay them flat to dry, this is simply my preference. The more socks you have, the less often you have to do laundry. We change our cutie's socks nightly. It worked for us to put a new pair of socks on each night at bedtime. Our cutie's feet were not very sweaty before she turned 1, so even in the summer months we didn't feel the need to switch her socks more frequently. If your child's socks feel damp, then you may need to change them more frequently.

Here are some options for you to explore:

- Black Robin Socks through MD Orthopaedics

  o These are the socks that work best for our daughter and the ones that we exclusively use with her today. A fellow mom recommended these socks to me. Picture 4.8 is my daughters' foot in this sock.

  o I ordered 6 pairs, 3 in one size and 3 in the next size up in preparation for the BnB transition.

  o They come in both single and double ply options, with rubber grips bottoms, knee high, an very soft.

  o They are expensive at $6.00 per pair.

  o They worked the best for us because they were the best fit and prevented blisters.

  o I recommend buying one pair to try out. See if they work for your cutie before investing in multiple pairs considering the price. Also, some babies need thinner socks, and thicker ones like these can cause more issues.

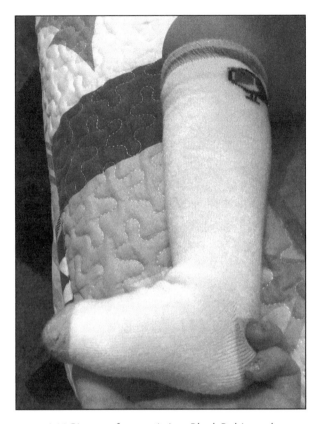

4.11 Picture of my cutie in a Black Robin sock.

- SmartKnit Kids-Amazon
  - o Seamless sensitivity socks.
  - o A parent posted on a Facebook page about these helping with their child's blisters.
  - o We bought one pair on Amazon but they were $11, which was almost double what we were used to paying.
  - o These socks were nice, and the seamless part was great, but they were too big for her little feet and bunched up underneath the boot, which could have caused other issues.

As she got bigger, they fit better but we didn't love them enough to buy a second pair.

- Walmart- Garanimals Brand Bobby Socks - We tried these when our cutie had red spots on her heels to see if a thinner sock would work. They worked fine but we ended up needing thicker socks.

- Target - Cat and Jack Brand Bobby Sock - We tried only one pair of these and were very similar to the Walmart brand.

- Judanzy- Judanzy.com - I bought a few pairs of these on Amazon in preparation for BnB, but I didn't do enough research to find the right fit. These socks didn't come up high enough for our cutie, so we didn't end up using them. Other parents have had success with them.

- Old Navy - Old Navy.com

- Children's Place - Basic Triple Roll Socks - in store and online

- Triple Roll socks- online only

- Gap Triple Roll - online

- Gymboree Brand Socks

Every baby has different skin and skin sensitivity. What works for one baby may not work for another. I recommend you have different options available to try. This will set you up for the most success. For example, a friend of mine never used Black Robin Socks because they were too thick for her baby, while we use them exclusively. You have to go with what works best for your baby and unfortunately you won't know that until you have begun BnB. Keep in mind that you may want to pre-order online-only socks, prior to starting BnB. Other socks that you can find at Target, Walmart, or Old Navy are easier to purchase in a pinch.

Other Supplies You Might Need

Here is a list of other supplies you may find helpful to maximize comfort and ease when using the BnB. These are all products that we used directly and had success with.

- Bodyglide Foot Anti-Blister Balm- Amazon or Target- We use this every time we put our cutie's boots on. It was recommended by the Clubhub website and we put a little bit of the glide on the back of her heels, the top of her foot where the foot meets the ankle and the tongue straps across the middle, and in the crease on the top of the big toe. We put it on any areas of redness elsewhere on her foot. I can't tell you for certain that it really helped prevent blisters, but it did a good enough job that we are still using it consistently to this date.

- Moleskin - Target

  o   We used this product to help prevent blisters on the heel and top of the foot. We put it on the boot rather than on the foot directly.

  o   There is a great video on the ClubHub website showing exactly how to use the moleskin and other items to provide protection for blisters. I highly recommend you watch it if you are interested.

- Pressure Saddles - MD Orthopaedics

  o   We used pressure saddles, nicknamed "Pringles," at first. For our cutie it created too much pressure in the front, which caused red spots on the back of the heel. *Much more about this in the blister section in Chapter 8.

  o   Many fellow clubfoot parents have expressed success with the pressure saddles to prevent blisters.

  o   Considering the cost, (approximately $8.00 for a pair) I think it is worth it to buy a pair and have on hand to use if needed.

4.12 Pressure Saddle from MD Orthopaedics

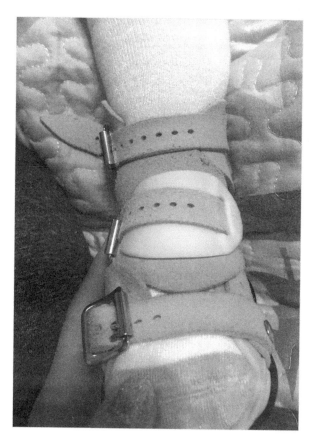

4.12a The pressure saddle on my cutie during 14-hour BnB wear

Walking Shoes

Holy cow, I cannot tell you how many shoes I bought for my cutie when she started standing and crawling around outside! I bought at least ten different pairs, and never seemed to find a shoe that was sturdy enough and small enough to fit her little feet. I wanted something to protect her feet when we were outside, because I worried about her cutting her foot and the subsequent issues of having to put on her BnB. As she got older, I wanted her to have a shoe she could comfortably stand in and also provided protection for feet. I felt like this shouldn't be too difficult, but it proved to be more of a challenge than I anticipated!

I love Target, and I spend a lot of time and money there, so I tried several different pairs of their shoe brands. The issue we ran into with Target brands was that they were always too big. Since our cutie had little feet, as many cuties typically do, the size that fit her (3-6month size) when she started walking, were not made for walkers. Three to 6-month-olds are typically not walking, therefore the shoes made for this size were simply for aesthetics or warmth. When our cutie first started walking it was summer and with two older and active sisters, she was outside a lot. I wanted to find some shoes that would protect her feet and encourage her walking. At her 14-month clubfoot checkup I asked her doctor for shoe recommendations and he said:

- Barefoot is best - For beginning walkers, having bare feet develops the strongest foot for walking. Anytime your cutie can have bare feet they should.

  o   This is true for all babies, not just clubfoot kids.

- Do not buy orthopedic shoes unless recommended specifically by your doctor. They are not needed for clubfoot kids whose feet are corrected.

- Any sneaker brand is good for ankle support. Our doctor did not prefer one brand over another.

  o   No Crocs. This was the one shoe type that our doctor did not recommend because it provides no ankle support.

- Wear shoes outside to protect feet from abrasions that could impact BnB wear.

Shoes we bought:

- Bunny slipper shoes - from Target - Used when she was crawling but not walking or pulling herself up on her own, to keep her feet warm.
  - o Not too tight but a protective layer
  - o No grippies on the bottom which made them easy to slip in
- Booties with fake fur inside - Target - Used when our cutie was pulling herself up and crawling, but not walking. These were sturdier and had a thicker bottom.
  - o Too warm during nice days as it was transitioning from winter to spring when she was wearing them.
  - o Used a hot glue gun on bottom to create grips for standing.
  - o Small enough to fit.
- Toms - Nordstrom Rack - Used when standing and using walker outside, but not when actually walking.
  - o A little too big even in the smallest size. Strap across the middle of the foot left occasional red marks.
  - o Fit better than the Target shoes and provided more support when she was walking with a walker.
- Stride Rite - Stride Rite Online - Used when she started walking and measured her feet to know the correct size.
  - o Used this brand with all 3 girls and beginning walking phase.
  - o Great and sturdy shoes that have lots of different options and sizes.

Fun Fact: You should not pass down shoes! This goes for all kids, not just cuties! As much as we appreciate hand-me-downs for our children, all feet are shaped differently and each child walks with a different gait. If your child wears a shoe that has been reshaped by another child's foot, the integrity of the structure is altered, and it can impair their walking. This can hurt their feet, legs and back. For all kids, new shoes are best.

When my cutie was not in her BnB she had bare feet 90% of the time. Her toes were free, unless it was very cold. Surprisingly I often heard comments from people about her bare feet such as: "Where are her socks?" "Aren't her feet cold?" and "Look at those free toes!" I didn't make much of these comments at the time, but looking back, I think that people were judging the fact that her feet were uncovered. Much like when someone asks where your child's coat is on a cold day, there's always a hint of judgement hidden in the comment.

I chose to respond in a few different ways. If someone I knew well made a comment, I would simply say, "Yeah those feet are covered enough and need as much free time as they can get!" The person usually got the hint and would respond with something like, "Oh yeah, good idea." If it was a passing stranger who commented, I went with something simple and said, "Yep, free feet are the happiest feet!" At this point, people didn't see her in her BnB, so they didn't know that for half the day she had her feet covered in double ply socks and buckled into boots. I didn't let their comments change my decision to leave her feet uncovered. It was my belief that those feet were covered enough and deserved to be free. I realize that not all people feel this way, but it was my choice, and if someone didn't agree, that was their issue, not mine.

How long should shoes fit?

- 10 months-3 years- 3-4 months

- 5 years and above- 5 to 6 months

- It's important to measure the size as cuties usually have smaller feet, and sometimes different sized feet, even in bilateral cuties.

The BnB can feel self-explanatory for experienced users, and after almost two years of use myself I can forget what it was like when we were first starting out. Don't be afraid to ask questions, to your doctor, your medical team, your friend circle, or anyone else that might be a resource for you during this time. The internet provides amazing resources for clubfoot families but if you can't find exactly what you are looking for, keep asking until you find the answers you need. The answers are out there, you may just have to search a little bit before finding them. I hope this chapter can also serve as a reference guide for all things boots and bar related, so if you are feeling confused flip back through this chapter and hopefully it will provide an answer or at least a place to search for the answer to your question!

CHAPTER 5

STRETCHING AND PHYSICAL THERAPY

ONCE YOUR CHILD TRANSITIONS TO **Boots and Bar,** you will be in charge of performing stretches 3-5 times a day on the foot with clubfoot, or both feet, if the condition is bilateral. Much like our journey with BnB, our experience with stretches changed when we switched doctors.

Discussed Topics:

- Stretching
- Ankle Stretches and Heel Stretches
  - o   Ankle Dorsiflexion
  - o   Ankle Inversion and Eversion
- Importance of Daily Stretching
- Dealing with Pushback
- Stretching in Public
- Adapting to Changing Needs

Our first experience was much more extensive than our second. Our first doctor worked with a physical therapist who showed us how to do these lengthy, detailed stretches in a span of 3 minutes. I can barely remember her showing us how to perform them. I should have taken a video of the physical therapist performing the stretches to use as a reference at home. We were, however, sent home with a packet of information explaining the stretches, but it didn't provide the answers to all our questions.

At this point in my life I had zero experience with physical therapy. I'd been fortunate enough to never experience physical therapy myself or help anyone else do it. This was a completely foreign topic to me, and I second-guessed myself *a lot* during those first few days. It definitely didn't alleviate my concerns when, for the first week of transition to BnB, our cutie screamed bloody murder every time my husband or I performed the stretches. She cried hysterically for the entire seven minutes. It is normal for your cutie to cry during this first few weeks of stretches because their feet are sensitive and stiff due to having been in the casts for so long. Our cutie cried for about the first week during every stretch session but then tapered off and was accustomed to it by week two. Some babies may take longer to adjust, but if your cutie is taking longer to adjust than you think is typical, or you think they are in real pain, then do not hesitate to contact your doctor to ask questions.

Stretches

At this point in your cutie's treatment your child's doctor will hopefully take some time to explain to you the benefits of performing the stretches daily. Our casting doctor explained what the stretches were but didn't give us a lot of background on why the stretches are important to maintain the correction of the foot. We were sent home with a packet of information about how to perform the stretches, which happened to include some information about the reason for the stretches. It was important for me to have a tangible reason for why we were doing stretches to hold on to in the moments when my cutie was screaming her head off.

Here are some of the main benefits of stretching that I remind myself of in moments of distress. Stretching

- Increases flexibility
- Improves strength
- Builds greater muscle tone

The daily stretching, 3-5 times a day to start, will help keep the tendons stretched, which is important to maintain your cutie's flexibility. You will work with your doctor to create your cutie's stretching routine, and it may be different than what we did with our cutie, but the most important thing is that you are doing some PT with your cutie every day.

Your doctor should work with you throughout your cutie's entire BnB phase to determine what stretches are necessary at different stages. You will continue to do some form of stretching until your child is 2-3 years old, but the frequency and type of stretching may change once your cutie's mobility increases, as they walk, run, and jump. Eventually your doctor will show you different active exercises your cutie can do on their own, instead of performing the stretches for them.

The following hints I found helpful from a handout provided by the team at Children's Hospital Colorado Multidisciplinary Clubfoot Clinic:

- The exercises should not be painful. Your baby should be able to eat and sleep normally.

- Your baby will adapt to treatment more easily when he or she is relaxed and exercises are done daily.

- Your baby's hip and knee should be bent during all exercises.

- Avoid twisting the knee.

- Only move your baby's foot during the exercises.

- The inner part of your baby's foot is strong and tight. The outer part of the foot is overstretched and weak. These exercises will stretch the inner part of the foot and strengthen the muscles on the outer part of the foot and leg.

Ankle and Heel Stretches

The first several weeks of stretches can be a struggle to get through as you and your baby adjust to the routine. You will become more confident in your ability to do the stretches correctly and your baby will become more comfortable with the process. You will also adjust to fitting the stretches into your baby's schedule. Let's face it, babies can have tough schedules and clubfoot babies are no different. Except our cuties have the added piece of BnB wear and stretches to deal with!

At first, during 23-hour wear, the stretches easily fit into our cutie's schedule because they were tacked on to the end of the free time. Since the free time was so short, the added stretches didn't feel like an extra step but another aspect of the free time. It wasn't until she decreased to 18-hour wear that we had to be conscious of fitting the stretches in 3 times a day. It didn't automatically have to be tacked on to the end of free time because the free time was much more extensive. We still tend to default to doing stretches before we put the boots back on, but you can do them right after boots are removed or in the middle of free time. There were days when I would do the stretches whenever we had some down-time and we were playing on the floor. Especially if I knew bedtime would be tight, as she was up longer than usual or it was bath night, because it would save those few extra minutes.

Note: Bedtime/nap time has an added layer of complexity (especially during 18-hour decreased wear) because you have to build in the extra time to get the BnB on and stretches done, if you do them before each bedtime like we did. When other babies are showing signs of sleepiness, you can put them to bed that minute. This isn't the case with our cuties. You will have to think ahead and add those extra minutes into your sched-ule so you can avoid an overtired baby.

As your baby grows, the stretches will get easier as you both grow in your comfort levels. But, things get more complicated when your baby starts to move and groove. It's amazing to see your baby hit developmen-tal milestones like rolling over, sitting up, army crawling, crawling, pulling up, cruising, and walking. Think back to when you were pregnant and you were told your baby would have clubfeet. What did you worry about? I definitely worried about my cutie not meeting her physical milestones. I wondered whether she would be delayed compared to my older girls.

My husband and I were so excited to watch her grow and begin mov-ing. It was pure joy, and we took so many videos of each movement, but we soon figured out that each movement milestone meant stretches be-came a little more difficult. If I had a quarter for every time my cutie tried to roll over in the middle of stretching, I can't tell you how much extra coffee fund money I would have! I often felt like I was wrestling with a squirmy pig and trying to get her to lie *still* takes a lot of work and distrac-tion. We try to do stretches in a place where I have lots of toys within arm's reach for distraction. If my older girls are around, I may enlist them to sing or play with her while I do the stretches.

Note: I learned that the full ABC song from A through "next time won't you sing with me," is about 40 count. So, I chose to sing the ABCs while stretching rather than counting. It was not only easier for me, and it was more interactive for our cutie.

There are other nursery rhymes that you could figure out the count to if you wanted to be creative, such as Itsy Bitsy Spider, and Twinkle Twinkle

Little Star, but you will have to count it out for yourself prior to trying it, so that you reach the 40 count accordingly.

While stretching can be time consuming and inconvenient, it can also be a special time for you to connect with your baby with lots of talking, eye contact, and interaction. If you choose to be purposeful and intentional with this time, it can be a wonderful bonding experience. I don't achieve this intentionality every time I do stretches with my cutie, because let's face it, life gets hectic and I have a lot of things running through my mind, as all of us moms do! But, when I do find the time to be intentional, it's a great opportunity to connect with my baby. My husband expressed that he feels more connected to our cutie as an infant than he did with our older girls, partly because of this devoted time with her. He was, and is, a direct participant in our cutie's treatment, and it has created a special bond between them because of the one-on-one attention needed to complete stretches and put BnB on.

Try to make stretches worthwhile by maintaining the integrity of each stretch instead of rushing through them. Our doctor said that fewer stretches done correctly are more effective than more stretches that are rushed through.

Following are the two main stretches recommended by Dr. Dobbs in his "A Parents Guide Through the Clubfoot Journey" handbook.

- Start slowly.

- Begin with 5 stretches on each foot with each stretch and then move up to 40 of each stretch on each foot.

- Dr. Dobbs recommends 5 times a day; we do 3 times a day. We did 3 times a day because that was the routine we had established before we switched doctors and Dr. Dobbs gave us the okay to continue.

Ankle Dorsiflexion

This stretch is focused on maintaining the flexibility of the heel of the foot (dorsiflexion). This dorsiflexion is typically achieved through the tenotomy, so you know your cutie went through something difficult to achieve it, and you want to ensure your child is able to maintain it. This stretch is also your best way to check in with your cutie's flexibility. If you are doing this stretch every day, you will know if something has changed as you will have months of reference.

Every time I have had a panic moment about my child's foot possibly relapsing (see the section below about push back), our doctor always requests a video or photo showing us performing this stretch on our cutie. It provides him with a direct baseline for where the flexibility of her foot is at, so that he can provide us with the most accurate assessment of her foot.

1. Lay Child on back

2. Place one hand on your baby's bent knee, grasp your baby's foot with the palm of your other hand, placing your index finger above the heel.

3. Now you can gently bend the ankle up and then point toes down.

4. Pull heel down and bend ankle as much as possible.

   Note: I put the heel of my hand on her whole bottom foot and push the toes upward, this gave me better leverage to stretch the ankle since I have smaller hands and couldn't flex as much with the index finger behind the heel. Our doctor saw this motion and okayed it for us.

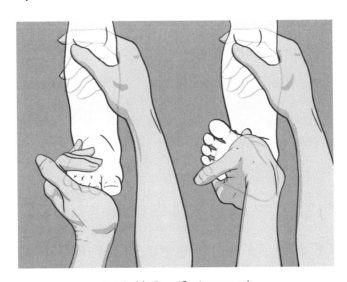

5.1 Ankle Dorsiflexion stretch

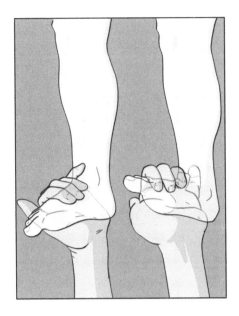

5.2 Ankle Dorsiflexion stretch

Ankle Inversion and Eversion

This stretch is focused on keeping this inside of the foot flexible and strengthening the outside of the foot.

1. Lay child on back

2. Stabilize the leg with one hand just above the ankle

3. At the base of the big toe use other hand to turn the foot out.

When we were taught how to do this stretch, we were shown that once you have pulled the foot out far enough you will see a white spot appear right next to her ankle. Once you see that spot you know you have turned the ankle far enough.

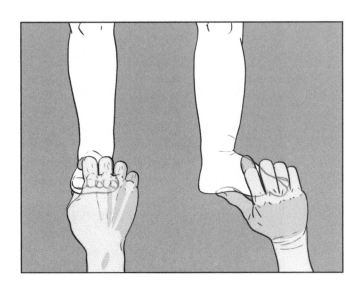

5.3 Ankle Eversion Stretch

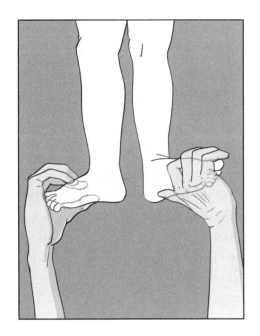

5.4 Ankle Eversion in stretched position

The Importance of Daily Stretching

I believe in the importance of stretching to maintain your cutie's flexibility and to get your hands on their feet several times a day. Our physical therapist stressed that "whatever you do, however many stretches you can do a day, *the most important thing* is to get your hands on their feet daily!" This is crucial because as caregivers we are the first line of defense against relapse and the best way to know if something changes is to get your hands on their feet every day. You will be the first person to know whether there has been a change in your cutie's flexibility because you are most familiar with how your child responds to stretches.

I have also heard, mainly through social media outlets, that stretches can help in a pinch if you forget your BnB while traveling or your child has to be out of BnB to let a blister or sore heal. If you ramp up the stretches, it can help maintain flexibility while out of the BnB for a night or two. Obviously, it is not recommended for your child to be out of BnB wear for any significant period of time, but as our physical therapist said, relapse doesn't happen in a day (or even two or three days). Relapse happens with frequent inconsistent use of the BnB, or incorrect use of the BnB over an extended period of time. Relapse can also happen as growth spurts impact the growth of your child's feet. Our cutie hasn't gone a night without BnB yet, but if that night comes, I will remember about doubling down on stretches for that period of time.

Dealing with Push Back

Sometime our cutie pushes back against the stretches. Her resistance seems to come in waves. Some months she didn't push against our hands at all during the dorsiflexion stretch and other months it felt like one foot or the other would actively fight the stretch. Our doctor told us that this is normal and that it only becomes an issue of flexibility if you can't flex their foot to the same degree when they are not fighting against your hand.

By "push back" I mean that she would physically push her foot against my hand and prevent me from getting her foot into a flexed position. Your doctor has probably told you that the most common sign of relapse is losing flexibility in the foot, especially during the first year before your child is walking. Therefore, it's totally normal for you to have a moment of panic if this happens with your cutie. As the first line of defense against relapse, you will know first whether there is a reason for concern.

When my cutie first pushed back, and it became difficult to get her foot into her normal flexion, I was worried. But then I remembered what our physical therapist told us. He suggested that we pop on a video if she started to push against the stretches. Our PT explained that the stronger our cutie got, the more likely it would be that she'd fight her stretches. He also relayed that a true reflection of flexion is how far you can flex the foot when she's not pushing against your hand. I was happy I'd tucked this advice in the back of my mind. It helped alleviate my worry when our cutie started resisting stretches. Stretches evolve throughout treatment as your child grows and changes. Go with your gut. If you think there is an issue, contact your doctor or their team with your concern, but if something changes during treatment also know that it can be a completely normal part of your child's development.

The first time our cutie pushed back was 2-3 months after she started BnB. She pushed back with one foot or the other, but not both simultaneously. She would resist with one foot for a period of time and then her foot would eventually relax. As I said before we usually did 40 reps of dorsiflexion holding for one second at a time, but during these periods of push back we would hold the flexion for up to 30 seconds once we were able to get her foot in the right position. Holding the foot felt more effective because we didn't want to spend time fighting to get her into the right position only to release it a second later. I think the push back is a good lesson in our own flexibility in treatment as parents. We have an expectation of how we want things to go, and most of the time treatment generally goes as planned, but it's good to be prepared for these variances.

Stretching in Public

We had to do our cutie's stretches in a number of places outside of our home: a park, a friend's house, the pool, at relatives homes, the zoo, the car…you get the drift. In many of these places we were surrounded by others; both those who knew about our cutie's clubfeet, and those who didn't. Inevitably, when I would do the stretches people would stare at us. Friends, family, and strangers would ask if the stretches hurt her, because frankly it looks like it hurts. Furthermore, if you tried stretching an adult's foot in this way, it would most certainly be unpleasant!

Generally, I chose to respond to these comments with a casual, "It doesn't look to be hurting her, does it?" This only worked if our cutie wasn't crying for one of millions of other reasons babies cry, not clubfoot related! Having to lie still, or being hungry, or tired, or wanting to be held, or colicky, or wanting the ball across the room that her sister was playing with. Other times, I went into more detail about the importance of stretching. I would briefly explain how stretching maintains the flexibility achieved through the tenotomy, and that not performing the stretches diligently was one of the most common reasons for relapse in the early years with a baby who has a corrected clubfoot. If you perform stretches with your cutie outside of your home, you will be looked at strangely, probably questioned, and possibly judged. In my opinion it's better to be prepared with a response for concerned onlookers rather than feeling flustered and put on the spot.

A close friend of mine, told me she couldn't watch me do the stretches with my cutie because it made her feel sick. Her comment probably should have hurt my feelings, but I knew I was doing the best thing for my baby and I was confident in doing it. You might have experienced something similar if you've had to use a NoseFrida or a bulb to suck a booger out of your baby's nose! It is gross and not pleasant to watch, and your baby probably screams, but you are doing what's best for your baby and other people's opinions be damned! Stretching is just like that, but clubfoot related! So, if it made my friend feel sick, she didn't have to watch. I was going to continue regardless of how anyone else felt because my baby was more important than their discomfort.

Stretching Through Play

As your cutie grows and becomes more mobile the static stretching that you have been doing (while your child is laying or sitting in a stationary position) may transition to look like stretching through play. We continued with the stationary stretching at least once per day and will continue until she absolutely fights it, but we have also added in some additional play focused stretching to encourage her flexibility. Our local Physical Therapist is an amazing resource for us (the same one that helped us during our cuties' casting phase with the local doctor) and he is very passionate about clubfeet and helping maintain flexibility through physical therapy.

During one appointment he mentioned that if our cutie started to really resist the stretching that we could add in some play focused activities to encourage flexibility. When he started to name off the various activities that we could try, I realized that our cutie already did most of the activities, largely due to the fact that she has two active older sisters who she desperately wants to imitate. Our cutie is constantly on the move and my husband and I swear she is going to be our most anxiety producing child because she really has no fear. If your cutie doesn't have older siblings that they are trying to keep up with here are a list of activities that our PT suggests to help with the stretching.

- Bear Crawling

- Walking up any type of ramp (bear crawling up ramp even better)

- Walk up a slide at a playground (with adult supervision).

- Walking on unstable surfaces such as a mattress or couch cushions

- Jumping on a mini trampoline with a bar to hold on to (with adult supervision).

- Standing on a ramp when in a stationary position (you can buy a foam pad and attach it to an ordinary stool that is used for handwashing/tooth brushing or eating at a counter).

This is not a comprehensive list, and I encourage you to be creative with it. If you think of a play activity that could double as an active stretch for your cutie, then try it and if it is successful and you feel comfortable, share with the clubfoot community. My husband and I have made the decision to continue with the stationary stretches for as long as our cutie allows, but I was relieved to know that there are alternative ways to get her stretching in if she absolutely fights it. I am not advocating for only stretching through play, but I do think that anything that helps provide a more well-rounded approach to treatment is helpful to many families.

Adapting to Changing Needs

Just like with any baby, it seems like once you've gotten into a successful routine, things are bound to change! For instance, once your baby has been sleeping soundly through the night for a few weeks, they start waking up at 4:00 a.m. for no apparent reason. Nothing has changed in your routine or your baby's diet, but your *baby* has changed. A baby experiences tremendous brain development in their first year. While your baby may still look the same on the outside, keep in mind that much is changing on the inside. The book, *The Wonder Weeks*, by Fans X. Plooij (Kiddy Owrld Promotions BV—The Netherlands: 2019) is an excellent resource that explains how much brain development occurs within the first year of life. Their rapidly developing brains, along with teething, illness, and physical development are bound to cause seemingly non-stop changes in your baby, so why wouldn't that include your baby's feet? So, if your cutie suddenly starts resisting their stretches, don't panic. Take a deep breath and check the overall flexibility of the foot before immediately contacting your doctor.

Babies change, and we have to try and remain flexible with them as much as we can. I remember when our cutie first started pulling herself up on furniture and pushing a walker around the house, her left heel would peel off the ground and she would stand on her toes in a stationary position. I started to feel the panic rise because I had read somewhere that toe walking was a sign of relapse, and I worried that toe standing counted as the same. Over the next week I watched her like a hawk and became more convinced that there was something wrong with the way she was standing. I decided to send pictures and a video to our doctor to double check. He responded by asking me to send clearer pictures and videos as well as a video of her dorsiflexion stretch. Well, my cutie was already asleep for the night when I received his request, and it was all I could do to not wake her up to take the videos.

I convinced myself that his response meant that he had seen something concerning while my husband rationally thought that he wanted a closer look before making an assessment. We sent the videos the following morning and waiting for his response felt like torture. It was either going to be that everything looked good or a request to see her in person to investigate further. Luckily, it turned out that he thought everything looked good and had no concerns regarding the toe standing. I was so relieved and also upset at myself for making such a big deal about it.

In hindsight, she was learning to stand up and support her weight and she was adjusting and developing like any normal baby would. She stopped toe standing several weeks later and continued to develop as normal through her standing and walking development. I needed to remember that babies need time to learn and grow and that might mean that things look a little different every day. I couldn't remember what my older two girls did when they learned to stand and walk because I didn't have anything to worry about. I didn't pay attention because I didn't care. It didn't matter if they stood on their toes because I didn't have anything to fixate on and also no frame of reference. Your cutie will challenge this for you as they develop because you will always be watching more carefully and looking for anything that could be a concern. I can promise that you will spend more time looking at and watching those little feet more than you ever thought you would. It will be a balance of vigilance and flexibility all the way through.

CHAPTER 6

MANAGING YOUR CHILD'S SCHEDULE

ONE OF THE ASPECTS OF **BnB** wear that I struggled with most was scheduling my cutie's day. It took a little while to find a rhythm that worked for us but maintained her free time, stretches, and extended 23-hour wear. I looked online for information about how other parents accomplished the free time schedule, and while I found out how people divided their time in general, I didn't find any visual outlines of their schedules. I'm a visual learner and extremely schedule oriented, so it would have been so helpful to me to see how other parents divided up their day during the different stages of BnB wear. This chapter provides samples of the schedules that worked for us. Of course, all schedules require some flexibility, but in general we found the following schedules worked well for us and met our cutie's needs.

Discussed Topics:

- 23-hour Wear
- 18-hour Wear
- 14-16-hour Wear
- 12-14-hour Wear

23-Hour Wear

When your cutie is in the 23-hour wear stage, the most challenging part of the schedule will be deciding when and how to break up the one hour of free time. Since your cutie will be in the BnB for the vast majority of the day, you won't have to spend time trying to figure out how they will get their BnB hours in (as you will with the decreased wear stages). We tried to stick with a consistent schedule during this phase because it provided stability for both our family and our cutie to have a known routine. But sometimes we had to deviate when the circumstances warranted it, like when we were out and about all day, and had to make a decision to either bank the middle of the day free time for later or tried to do it wherever we were (the zoo, pool, or park). The following is the main schedule that worked for us:

Sample Schedule

6:00-6:30am	Wake up, feed (bottle or breast feed)
6:45-7:00am	Start first free time (boots off)
7:05-7:20am	Begin stretches
7:15-7:30am	BnB back on
7:30-9:30am	BnB wear time
9:30am	Diaper change/boot check
9:45-1:00pm	BnB wear time
1:00pm	Start second free time (boots off)
1:20pm	Begin second set of stretches
1:30pm	BnB back on
1:30-3:30pm	BnB wear time
3:30pm	Diaper change/ boot check*
3:45-5:30	BnB wear time
5:30pm	Start third free time (boots off)
5:50pm	Begin third set of stretches
6:00pm	BnB back on and bedtime

Free Time

We intentionally scheduled 20 minutes of free time prior to bedtime so that it became part of her bedtime routine, including putting on the BnB, that we could use for the years to come. We usually did her bedtime stretches in whichever room she was sleeping in, which was still our room during the 23-hour wear stage. Our cutie's pre-bedtime free time was generally done around dinner time, in our living room. This way she could play on her mat and be active with the family.

Some families choose to do 15 minutes of free time 4 times a day instead of 20 minutes 3 times a day. For us the 20 minutes already felt like such a short period of time that decreasing by 5 minutes felt like almost no time at all. It also meant having to fit another free time into the schedule which seemed overwhelming. I recommend trying various schedules, and being flexible to switch things around, especially in the beginning while everyone is adjusting to the schedule. If the 20 minutes of free time isn't working for you, try the 15-minute schedule and see if it makes a difference.

Bath Days

On the nights that we gave our cutie a bath we would usually bank a 20-minute section to add on to her last free time so that we didn't have to rush through bath time. We would bank either 10-20 minutes for the bath so that we would at least have 30 minutes for free time and bath, otherwise it felt like we were rushing through the bath and felt stressed about the free time. You could also decrease each free time to only 15 minutes and have 30 minutes for bath at the end of the day.

Our cutie enjoys bath time, so it was worth it to skip that midday free time to give her more time in the bath. Some cuties don't enjoy bath time. If this is the case, you may just tack on a 5-minute bath at the end of your nighttime free time and keep the midday free time. Additionally, some babies have ultra-sensitive skin after the casts are removed and may just need time to adjust to the bath after the casts. Some cuties may resist their first couple of baths but then grow to enjoy them so keep giving it a try. If and when your cutie starts enjoying more time in the tub, you can adjust the schedule to allow for more time as needed.

Boot Checks

A "boot check" is simply our term for taking our cutie's boots off and checking the feet for red spots and blisters. This was intentionally done twice a day, on top of the 3 free times. Our casting doctor suggested we do these checks so that we got used to putting the boots on and so our cutie could get used to having them put on. If the feet had any significant red spots of signs of blisters, we would readjust the boot, put on more foot glide, or a blister bandaid and keep an eye on it during future free time. (More on blisters in Chapter 8: Handling Skin Issues.)

Bedtime Routine

For the first few weeks of BnB transition, it might be helpful to plan to have your support person there for the bedtime routine. When my husband was home, we could each take a foot for stretches and boot placement, which decreased the overall crying time. Sometimes he would handle our older daughters' bedtime while I was able to focus on our cutie's routine.

For us, the bedtime routine was and has remained important to maintain consistency. We did her bedtime routine in the same place every night. Our cutie loved her bedtime routine, and this has created a positive association with bedtime. This was a place that she never spent time otherwise throughout the day, so it was a good indicator to her of what was coming. We didn't do this intentionally at first, it was just the most convenient and comfortable place to do bedtime and the routine seemed to work for all of us. If you can create a similar routine for your baby, it can help foster positive associations with putting on the BnB as your cutie gets older.

18-Hour Schedule

Switching to a decreased schedule is exciting! I remember being thrilled to have more flexibility in our schedule and happy that our baby could have more time out of the BnB. But we found this freedom was unexpectedly overwhelming. Yes, our cutie got more free time, but I also had to figure out how to fit that free time into our schedule. This proved a challenge for me because our cutie has two older sisters that have busy school and activity schedules that we had to work around.

When it came time to decrease hours, our BnB doctor told us to double up the free time for a week, double it up again for the next week, and again until we had the full 6 hours of free time. Since we were doing 20 minutes of free time, we doubled to 40 minutes 3 times a day for the first week. Our cutie was now getting two hours of free time a day, and let me tell you, it felt magical! I actually had time to get things done, and she had time to roll and play to her heart's content.

For us, the mornings were often busy, filled with the bustle of getting ready for the day. 40 minutes worked well for our cutie, because it was just enough free time before we had to put her in her car seat and take her older sisters to school. At this time, she was 5 months old, so she didn't have any semblance of a nap schedule other than being awake for a two hour stretch before needing to go to sleep again. Our rule during 18-hour wear was that if our cutie was in her car seat, she would be in her BnB, in case she fell asleep. Because we followed this rule there were some days that she didn't get the full 6 hours free.

The next week, we doubled her free time again to 80 minutes 3 times a day (4 hours a day free). An 80-minute stretch was too long for our cutie in the morning, because she wasn't usually awake for that amount of time before we had to hit the road. In general, we would bank whatever time we lost in the morning and tack it onto the second or third free time block. We usually banked most of our free time for before bed, because, like many babies, that was her "witching hour," and she tended to be slightly happier when she was BnB-free.

In the final transition week, we could use the full 6 hours. We could do three two-hour blocks of time, but we rarely had a full two-hour block where she wasn't either napping or in the car seat, so we had to figure out other chunks of time. We usually aimed for four 90-minute blocks of time but inevitably these were cut short and we didn't meet the full 6 hours.

We liked to bank any unused time for the end of the day, but sometimes that backfired because we banked too much time and had to cut her free time block short for bedtime. It might take a little while before you find the schedule that fits you and your cutie. Maybe your cutie is your first kiddo and you won't have the restraints of school drop off and pick-ups. Or, maybe your cutie is in full time daycare and you'll need to coordinate with your daycare provider on a schedule that works for everyone.

Sample 18-Hour Schedule:

6:00am	Wake up boots off
6:00-7:20am	Free time- no BnB
7:20am	Stretches and boots on
7:30am	BnB on for car seat time and short nap
9:00am	Boots off
10:20am	Stretches and boots on

10:30am	Boots on and second nap and car seat time
1:00pm	Boots off and free time
2:20pm	Boots back on for last nap and car seat time
4:30pm	Boots off for last 90-minute free time
5:50pm	Stretches, bedtime routine and BnB back on
6:00pm	Bedtime and 12-hour stretch of full BnB wear

On bath nights we would fit bath into the last block of 90 minutes of free time.

Our doctor told us to double up the free time over the span of several weeks so that our cutie would have an easier transition. As discussed previously, there are variances in how doctors suggest you decrease hours and your schedule may look different than ours. I wanted to give you a visual break down of our experience, but this is a guide and not a rule. If your cutie's schedule differs, then utilize the schedule as a reference point to create your own schedule. It was also a hard and fast rule for us that if our cutie was sleeping, she needed to have her BnB on, whether in the car seat or crib. We wanted her to have her boots on during her most immobile times, therefore she wouldn't lose any free time that would allow her to move and groove.

14-16 Hour Schedule:

After doing the three-month, 18-hour wear schedule, we got the go ahead to move down to 14-16 hour wear at the 8 month mark. During this transition, we didn't decrease time by doubling up. We went directly to a "night and nap" schedule, which usually averaged out around 15 hours for us. We always made sure our cutie was in the BnB for at least 14 hours at a minimum.

Sample 14-16 Hour Schedule:

6:00am	Wake up BnB off
8:45am	Stretches and BnB on
9:00am	Nap in BnB
10:30am	Wake up BnB off
12:45pm	Stretches and BnB on
1:00pm	Nap BnB on

2:30pm	Wake up BnB off
5:45pm	Stretches, bedtime BnB on
6:00pm	Bedtime 12-hour BnB wear

Babies nap and sleep on different schedules, and you'll have to maintain some flexibility, but once we hit the nine-month mark our cutie moved into a more predictable two-nap schedule, with three hour stretches of awake time in between. At this point we also stopped putting her BnB on when she was in the car seat. This meant that sometimes we did a song and dance (literally) to keep her awake during the school shuffle to ensure that she would nap at home.

Pros: More consistent naps

Cons: Having to be home for naps meant no more sleeping while traveling.

Car seat naps became very short at this point, so this became a last resort.

12-14 Hour Wear

We didn't start 12-hour wear until our cutie was 14 months old, because we didn't have her 1 year check up until then. Our doctor told us to keep the 14-16 hour wear until we saw him at the next appointment. At 14 months our cutie was transitioning from two naps to one nap a day, so when we went down to 12-14 hour wear, we had different schedules based on whether she slept for one or two naps that day. Our doctor said that at 1 year we could transition to 12-hour wear, meaning that if our cutie had the BnB on for 12 hours at night then she didn't have to wear them during nap time. We decided that to maintain consistency, whenever she was sleeping in the crib, she would have the BnB on, whether night or nap. At this point we made the decision to let her sleep in the car seat without the BnB without any hesitation as these naps were usually 30 mins or less.

Sample Schedule with 2 Naps

5:30am	Wake up but stays in crib
6:00am	Out of crib and BnB off
8:30am	Nap in Crib with BnB
10:00am	Out of BnB

2:00pm	Nap in Crib with BnB
3:30pm	Out of BnB
6:30pm	Bedtime and BnB on

Sample Schedule with 1 Nap

5:30am	Wake up but stays in Crib
6:00am	Out of crib and BnB off
8:30am	Short nap in car (20-30 mins) no BnB
9:00am	Wake up
12:30pm	Nap time with BnB in crib
2:30pm	Wake up and BnB off
6:30pm	Bedtime and BnB on.

I didn't include stretches in these 12-hour wear schedules because as your cutie begins to walk, your stretches may change, and you will most likely have more flexibility in your schedule for when you want to do stretches. When our cutie first started 12-14 hour wear, she had just begun walking (my definition for when my babies were "actually" walking and not just taking steps, was when they walked more than they crawled), and we moved to doing the stretches twice a day.

We did the stretches before her BnB went on at both nap and night. As she got older and more mobile (which provided her with active stretching throughout the day) we went down to stretches once a day, before night-time wear, simple because she was fighting the stretches so much. By fighting it I mean that she didn't want to be still long enough for us to per-form the stretches. My other clubfoot moms still do stretches with their cuties' 2-3 times a day. Some parents find it is easiest to get the stretches in during inactive times, such as when your cutie is in the highchair, that way they are contained and naturally distracted by eating. I suggest that whatever time you can to fit the stretches in, you do it.

CHAPTER 7

SLEEPING

I DREADED WRITING ABOUT THIS TOPIC because I feel like a total failure in the sleep department. I don't think my husband and I ever figured out the sleeping thing with our babies. Not just with our cutie, but with either of our older girls as well. If this book is supposed to be helpful and I feel like a total disaster on this topic, what right do I have to write about it? What will you gain from reading about how my husband and I barely got any sleep for almost 9 months? How can I impart words of wisdom if there were moments when I was so exhausted my face felt numb? I literally couldn't feel the right side of my face one morning, and my mom thought I was having a stroke. Nope, no stroke; I was just utterly exhausted.

I contemplated skipping this entire section and instead simply recommending products that (semi) worked for us. That should be sufficient, right? This way you could get some information without me terrifying you with stories of sleepless night after sleepless night. I could also maintain the illusion of imparting helpful advice to other clubfoot parents. I could still fool you! I went as far as talking to my therapist about how desperately I was avoiding writing about sleep. Which was probably the best idea I had in the sleep department, because my therapist is wise and reminded me that the real help comes from honesty. The reason I decided to write this book was so that other parents could read about our journey and find some helpful tips, but also so they don't feel like they are going it alone. Clubfoot treatment can be stifling and isolating, and waxing poetic about how much I know about helping your baby sleep isn't going to be of any help to you. This is me keeping it real. Here is the hard truth of our first-year struggles with sleep, in the hopes that you will find some comfort in having a much better experience or solace if you are going through anything similar.

This chapter discusses:

- Our sleep struggles
- Developing sleep habits
- Our version of crying it out
- Finding patience and grace
- Importance of BnB wear during sleep
- Sleep aids

Our Sleep Struggles

Our cutie's sleep troubles didn't begin until about three weeks after she transitioned to BnB and about three days after her "two" month immunizations (which were really done at three months old). Throughout her first 3 months she slept like a normal newborn, other than the nights she got a new cast. I won't say she slept like "a champ" because, like most newborns, she never slept through the night. But she was a solid "average" sleeper. Our cutie could sleep in four-hour stretches without nursing, but around the 3-month mark something flipped.

I honestly can't tell you why this happened, but within that next month she progressively got worse at sleeping. Sure, it could have been the infamous 4-month-old sleep regression or maybe developmental changes, like learning to roll over (quite the feat with a BnB on I might add), or maybe it was the BnB wear in general. We will never really know the cause, only that our cutie was waking up every 1-2 hours, every night, and was unable to soothe herself back to sleep. I can't tell you how many times a night she woke up because all the nights blur together in a hazy fog, but I do know that I slept for a solid six hour stretch only one night in nine months. In general, I slept only 1-2 hours at any given time. Also, I wasn't the only one handling these night-time wakings! My husband would take shifts so that I could get any little stretch of sleep. I have a pretty good memory, but I cannot give you details of what nights were like during this time, only that my overall feeling was of complete and total exhaustion.

Developing Sleep Habits

While we definitely didn't have anything figured out sleep-wise, there were principles that we followed with our older girls that applied to our cutie too:

- We were not co-sleepers, or bed-sharers, with any of our girls. Other than those few nights with the new cast. The majority of the night our baby slept right next to us in a Rock and Play for the first 5 months.

- We did not put our babies down in their crib when they were still awake. We would rock them, bounce them, feed them until they were fully asleep and then put them down.

- We did not try the "cry it out" method with any of our girls, especially not before the age of 10-11 months.

- We adhered to early bedtimes–6:00 or 7:00 pm at the latest--with a stretch of awake time right before bedtime.

- Plenty of breastfeeding/bottles in the middle of the night until almost the age of 2.

We followed the same guidelines with our cutie, but there was an extra emotional component because she had to sleep in the BnB. I felt a lot of guilt that she had to sleep in her BnB and she was just expected to "figure it out." This guilt propelled me to do more to try to soothe her. I bounced her, rocked her, held her and nursed her for longer because I wanted to do anything to help alleviate any perceived discomfort.

I don't know whether she was actually experiencing discomfort from wearing her BnB. But she couldn't tell me what was bothering her, and there was an extra set of possible issues that we had to contend with. What if she was crying because her heel had slipped up? Or, what if her sock was bunched up? What if the middle buckle was too tight? Or, what if it was too loose? The 'what ifs' were endless! I wanted to do anything I could to help comfort her, but I didn't know what the issue was. It felt like I was playing a never-ending game of guess and check where the answers were never revealed! My suggestion is that you and your partner come up with some overall guidelines for sleep that you can try to adhere to. They may be very different than the ones I have listed, but if you have an overall idea of what you do and don't want for sleep, and what you are willing and unwilling to try, it can help be a guidepost for what is already a difficult situation.

Our Version of Crying It Out

At some point, I forced myself to stop playing the "what if" game and focus on the things that would help her sleep, which ultimately meant letting her cry. We had attempted every other option and nothing else worked, so we had to let her cry a little so she could figure out how to soothe herself. But I felt absolutely terrible about it. Was I really going to let my baby, who was essentially strapped into hiking boots with a bar attached, just "figure it out?" What kind of mother does this? The answer is: a desperate one. A mother who had exhausted all other options for months. A mother who needed to be a functioning mom to her two older girls. A mother who had to consider the possibility that her cutie needed some time to work through falling asleep on her own.

Our version of crying it out looked more like letting our cutie cry for 5-10 minutes before eventually falling asleep. This was a mad cry, not a sad cry. What is the difference between the two, you might wonder? Simple, mad crying was screaming with no real tears, and a sad cry meant real tears. We had to accept the fact that our cutie was frustrated and no matter how much we tried to help her by rocking, bouncing, and nursing, nothing was helping her figure out that frustration. Honestly, she had to work it out on her own (some). This didn't mean we let our cutie cry for hours on end without checking in on her, but we also didn't rush in the minute we heard her cry. We started to give it two, then three, and then 5 minutes before we checked on her, and then we extended this delay as she adjusted. My husband would go into her room, lay her back down, and say firmly, "It's time for sleep. Night night," so that she would pick up on it as another sleep cue. Some nights were better than others. We just did what felt right depending on her cry and how she was feeling.

In the first year of our cutie's life she had two rounds of a stomach bug that lasted four weeks at a time. This caused her to need several diaper changes a night. Those weeks were hard because we needed to check to make sure she didn't need a diaper change. Those weeks felt endless. She also had a couple of colds that made it difficult for her to settle, and we would hold and rock her for significantly longer to help her get into a deeper sleep. It was much harder to try and let her self-soothe when she wasn't feeling well, but even on those nights we sometimes had to put her down because nothing we tried worked.

Those 9 months of very little sleep almost broke me — physically from exhaustion and emotionally from guilt. I wanted so desperately to help our cutie sleep and figure out a way to soothe her, but nothing seemed to work. I would have held her in the rocking chair for hours if it would have soothed her, but she always needed fast movement like bouncing, and I swear, you can only do that for so long! Many times during the night and her nap times, I became overwhelmed with frustration. When this happened, I had to put her down just to take a breather. I did so much more bouncing and rocking than with my older girls because I felt guilty that she had to sleep in her BnB. I knew that *she* didn't know any different, but that didn't make me feel better about it.

I didn't feel bad about putting on the BnB because I knew that it was the best thing for my daughter. Also, I never considered letting her go BnB-free for a night to give us all a break, because I knew that it would only make things harder in the long run. The BnB is what keeps my cutie's feet in the place we worked so hard to get during casting, and endless nights of minimal sleep were not going to stop me from keeping my eye on the prize. It was my job to keep those feet in place as much as I could, and I wasn't going to let anything get in the way of that. That doesn't mean that it wasn't hard, because it was. It doesn't mean that there weren't days when I wanted to curl up in a ball and cry myself to sleep, because I did. But it did mean that I wouldn't stop trying. I wouldn't give up. I would do everything in my power to give my daughter every chance in the world to be anything she wanted. Watching her learn to stand by herself and take her first steps are some of the greatest joys I have experienced in my life. It made it all completely worth it, every minute of lost sleep, to see her keep moving forward, step by little step.

Finding Patience and Grace

I am certain there are many things we could have done to improve her sleep, but we did the best we could in the moment. I spent hours online researching sleep regression and cry it out methods. I even emailed her doctor about the possibility of the BnB hurting her. I tried a lot of different things in the hopes that her sleep would improve, and I would start to feel human again, but nothing seemed to do the trick. Yes, we could have tried letting her cry it out much earlier than we did, but I didn't want to. You could be reading this and thinking of 20 different options I could have tried, and to that I say, I truly hope they work for your cutie! At the time, I was open to different ideas, and would try them, but we inevitably fell back into old habits. I do remember people would suggest contacting a sleep consultant and I felt like laughing, because what does a sleep consultant know about helping a baby sleep with BnB? Maybe I am wrong, and some sleep consultants do have experience with it, but I never felt like someone would be truly able to understand. If I'm being honest with myself, I think it was more emotional reasons holding me back from seeking help than anything. I didn't want someone to feel sorry for our daughter and then make me defensive about it. I didn't want to explain the whole situation and discuss my emotional process with someone else. I think in the end I really didn't think they would understand how complex it all felt, so I just didn't try.

I am definitely not saying that you should follow our lead, almost the opposite! You should find whatever works for you and your cutie best. I hope that you find a rhythm that works much better than ours and that sleep isn't a struggle for you! But, if you are anything like us and feel like you can't figure it out no matter which approach you take, I hope you find comfort in knowing that you're not alone and that you will survive. I can't even give you specific advice on how to survive, but just know that I did, and that means that you can too. These are the things that I wish I could go back and tell myself during that time and hopefully they'll help you if you're struggling as well:

- Grace - Give yourself and your cutie grace through this stressful time. Walk away and take a break if you need it, take a few deep breaths and remind yourself to give yourself grace.

- Survive not thrive - Maybe I wasn't thriving every day, but I did survive. Maybe my older two had too much screen time and I drank too much coffee, but we survived. I can focus on thriving when I get more sleep.

- It will get better - After our cutie reached the age of one, her sleep improved significantly. It's not perfect, but it has gotten better.

- Progress not perfection - By progress I mean her feet. Every night you are making progress toward the end goal of maintaining correction and eventually getting out of BnB. The ongoing progression might mean that things are not going to be perfect. Sleep wasn't perfect, but every night was progress.

- You will live - This might be similar to surviving but I remember a therapist told me when I was struggling through a major insomnia bout, that I would live. If I didn't sleep for a night or even 4 nights, I would live. She was right, I did live, and I promise you will too.

So there it is, the real truth of our experience with sleep and BnB. I am not sure it will be of any use other than encouraging those who are in the thick of it and providing prayers of gratitude to those who are in a much better place.

Importance of BnB Wear During Sleep

It is vital that your cutie learn how to sleep in their BnB. Sleep wear is the most important aspect of BnB wear, because this is when your cutie will be wearing the BnB the most. It is not an option to simply take your cutie out of their BnB in order to get some sleep, at least not consistently.

My cutie has never slept in her crib without her BnB on. Until we went down to 14-hour wear, she never slept with her BnB off period. Whether she slept in the car seat, stroller, or crib, she had her BnB on. In the book, "Clubfoot: The Quest for a Better Life for Millions of Children," Dr. Cook mentioned that Dr. Ponseti frequently said that a clubfoot, "will not easily give up its crooked ways" (2019, p.117). If parents do not comply with the BnB wear schedule, the child's foot will want to return to its original clubbed position. This means your cutie has to learn to sleep in the BnB. If you want to give your child the best chance of avoiding relapse, it is vital they learn to sleep in the BnB.

I found myself asking why during sleep? What if we did the BnB during the day instead of night, would it have the same result as long as my cutie was in the BnB for the required hours? In a way the answer seems obvious because sleep is when a child is least active and who wants to try and keep a walking toddler in BnB for an extended period of time when they are awake? As I was contemplating these questions, I read the section in

Dr. Cook's book that states, "When a child begins to crawl and walk, the affected structures have opportunities to stretch and strengthen. But during inactivity, mostly at night and during nap, the internal forces in the muscles, tendons and ligaments have the greatest chance of returning the foot to its original state" (2019, p.117). So it is not just that the chunk of sleep hours are the easiest way to get your 12 hours in BnB done, but it is the actual inactivity that causes the greatest opportunity for relapse. When your cutie is active, running, jumping, playing, they are working those feet to the max, and this work is naturally strengthening those piggies, so they have to keep doing it. That means when they are not working them, those feet want to move back to where they started.

At some point--maybe before she was even born, maybe it was during research of clubfoot treatment, or when I held my baby for the first time--I made the decision that I would do whatever was necessary to help her through her treatment. To me, that meant being brave and not giving up. Let me clarify that "never giving up" doesn't mean that you shouldn't take breaks, find ways to care for yourself, and ask for help. Never giving up means that in the face of adversity you choose to keep moving forward, moment by moment, step by step, because there will be an end. If you need a solid night of sleep, ask your partner or a friend to come and help you, but don't lose sight of the end goal. I knew that if I took my cutie's BnB off just once, that it would be a slippery slope that might open me up to allowing myself and my baby some respite from something we could never really have long term respite from.

We never had an issue where we needed to leave the boots off for a medical reason, such as letting a blister or pressure sore heal. If this is your situation, I suggest working through it with your medical professional directly. And maybe you don't agree with me! Perhaps you can allow your cutie to go BnB-free for a night or two in order to get some much-needed rest, knowing that you'll come back stronger and be able to keep your resolve long-term. You have to know who you are and what you're capable of doing.

Sleep Aids

This section provides a list of sleep items that we tried, with varying degrees of success, but might help you find a magic combination for your cutie.

- **Rock and Play-Self rocking** - purchased at Target* - We used this during the casting phase and the transition to BnB. We used the regular Rock and Play with both of my older girls until they got too big and then we transitioned to their crib (both roughly around 4 months). We upgraded to the self-rocking just to help soothe without so much effort on our part.

  o We would put a rolled up receiving blanket under the BnB in the Rock and Play to support the BnB, but this Rock and Play also naturally elevates the feet which was another benefit.

  o We transitioned her out of this when she started to roll over on her own at about 4-5 months. She had pretty much outgrown it and we knew it was a safety hazard if she could roll in it.

Note: We used this product before the recall occurred and it was taken off the market. I always recommend you do your own research and determine if this is a safe product for you and your child. I deemed it was because whenever she slept in it, I was always right next to her and when she was old enough to roll, we moved her out of it. But that decision is entirely up to you and your partner and I am not suggesting you use a product that you may not feel is safe. You have to make the right decision for you and that might mean going a different route.

- **Boppy Lounger Pillow** - purchased at Target - Our daughter starting using this during sleep and naptime after her first birthday, and still sleeps with it every night. When we transitioned from the Rock and Play to the crib this helped her feel cuddled and stopped her from rolling over in the swaddle. At this point we were still using a swaddle that was not safe for her to roll in, so the lounger helped keep her from rolling around as much. She wasn't ready to lose the swaddle, so we stuck with this for a while.

  Note: It is not recommended that you let your baby sleep in the lounger, and it is a decision that you have to make about the safety of your baby. By the time our cutie started rolling over in the crib and using the lounger more as a pillow, I was confident that she was strong enough to move herself out if she was not comfortable.

One negative is that there is not a cover for the lounger like there is for the nursing pillow, so if you want to wash the pillow then you have to wash and dry the entire pillow which is cumbersome and can take a long time. We had to do this once when our daughter threw up all over the pillow and we needed to clean it immediately, it took about half a day for it to clean and dry. If you do put it in the dryer, make sure you put a tennis ball wrapped in a pillowcase in the dryer too so that the pillow will keep its shape.

- **Embe Swaddle** - Purchased 2 on Amazon - This swaddle is a serious Godsend for clubfoot cuties because it provides the option to have legs out! No other swaddle worked during the casting phase, and our daughter needed to be swaddled.

It was easy to use with a zipper in the middle that zipped from top to bottom as not to cause discomfort on the neck, and the middle portion where the feet could go inside, was then able to snap onto the chest, and then wrapped another piece entirely around. Our daughter never escaped, and it made diaper changes easy. There are several different snap areas so as your baby grows you can adjust how far up or down you need the middle portion to be.

- o   We purchased 2 because our cutie had reflux and was prone to spitting up and it was always useful to have a backup.

- o   We used this swaddle throughout the first transition to BnB, because she was already used to it and it worked equally well with the boots and bar as it did with the casts.

- o   We had to make sure that she had her legs covered at night with pajamas, because they were not covered by the swaddle itself. We loved these so much that we were sad when our daughter outgrew them!

- **Halo Sleepsack Swaddle** - hand-me down from a friend – We found this brand was not tight enough for our little Houdini, who easily broke free! The larger sizes of this brand have enough room in the bottom of the bag to accommodate the BnB.

- **Anna and Eve Swaddle Strap Arms Only** - Purchased on Amazon - My best friend found this product on Amazon for us when our daughter was too big for the Embe but still needed her arms swaddled tight and her feet free.

- o   We purchased the size large, because at this point our daughter was 5-6 months old. This swaddle worked well, and our cutie rarely escaped from it (those little hands were still very distracting).

- o   We used this swaddle from about 5 old months through 10 months old. We had to stop using it when she started to actively fight to get out of the swaddle. She also started to roll in her crib around 10 months and we didn't want her to roll onto her stomach with no arms to be able to push herself up or roll back.

- **Zipadeezip** – Purchased on Amazon - We moved to this swaddle at 10 months when she started to fight the other swaddle and roll over in her crib. The base is big enough to accommodate the BnB in the size medium (6-12 months old). She could safely roll around in it and use her arms to push herself up and it works as a blanket to provide warmth. It allowed her arms to move freely but kept her hands covered, so that they weren't distracting.

  - o   Acts as a great sleep cue as she gets older because when we put her in it, she knows that it's time for sleep (or at least I tell myself that!).

  - o   The larger size (12-18 months) is significantly larger than the medium. We transitioned to this when she was about 14 months and used it until she was 2.

  - o   Our daughter is still using this brand at this time and we plan to keep her in it as long as she still likes it.

  - o   One negative is that it zips from bottom to top, so it makes diaper changes in the middle of the night more cumbersome because you have to pull the BnB out completely. It also makes checking the heel placement of the foot harder as you can't sneak up the zipper and stick your finger in to feel or even look through the heel hole.

- **Hiccapop Day Dreamer Sleeper Baby Lounger** - Amazon - We didn't use this exact product but something similar that a fellow clubfoot mom had given us. We used it to help transition from the Rock and Play to the Crib. We didn't use it for very long because our cutie seemed to outgrow it quickly, but we used it around the house, such as when I needed to bathe my older girls. It was good for reflux because it was at an incline and helped prop her up. The incline also helped take some pressure off the BnB.

- **Leacho Podcaster** - Amazon - This item seems similar to the Boppy Pillow lounger but with a deeper middle. We didn't use it, but it was recommended by a fellow clubfoot parent for the casting phase but based on our success with the Boppy Lounger it would probably be good for BnB too. It is more expensive than the Boppy Product.

- **Doc-A-Tot** - Amazon or Doc-A-Tot website - This is a portable bed that can be placed anywhere to create a contained sleep environment. We didn't use this either, but other fellow clubfoot moms recommended it.

  o   My best friend bought one for her daughter, who doesn't have clubfoot but does have other unique sleep needs, and really liked it.

  o   It comes in a larger version that can be used for older kiddos.

  o   It is a more expensive product, especially the larger version, which can be more difficult to find. If you are interested in trying it, you might look for a sale or ask to borrow one from a friend if they have one, to try before you commit to buying.

  o   This product is supervised sleep recommended, much like the Bobby Lounger and you will have to make your best judgement about how to use this product with your cutie.

- **Exercise Ball** - Amazon - Exercise Ball Professional Grade - We use this several times a day to help our cutie calm down and go to sleep. We didn't use it during the casting phase of treatment, because I didn't want the casts to bang against one another, but once we started BnB it worked well.

- o Bouncing her on this ball was one of the only ways to calm her down even when she wasn't sleepy. We used it so much that we had one in her room for "official" naps and one in the living room for calming down. We deflated it and brought it with us on any trip where we would be sleeping somewhere different. We used the first one so much that it popped, and we had to buy another one. Just be careful if you are ordering online to get the correct size because I accidentally bought one that was the right size for my 5-year-old.

- o We still use it today to put her to sleep. There is something about the rhythmic bouncing that helps settle her down and soothe her to sleep.

- **Crib Bumper Pads** - Amazon - Tillyou Quilted Breathable Crib Bumper Pads - Once our daughter was in the crib and moving, we wanted something to help when her BnB banged against the crib. With our other daughters we used the breathable ones, but I wanted something thicker but still safe. We eventually landed on this one. It is a good mix between breathable and regular bumper pads.

Sleep aids are so helpful when they work, but when they don't, they can cause even more frustration. What new parent hasn't purchased a product with the hope that it will magically help their child sleep? I think the answer is not many (or none frankly). Whether it be a sleep sack, a swaddle, a bassinet, or a sound machine, there is always a glimmer of hope that this will be the product that truly is the game changer? I literally bought the nested bean swaddle with this exact goal in mind, because when you are exhausted to the point of no return, you will literally try or buy anything to help your baby sleep!

The truth is a certain product may provide some help, but it will probably not be the game changer that you are hoping for, especially for our cuties. These little ones have different needs and the products that will work for them may seem limited, but the reality is that they may have complicated sleep until they are done with their BnB. We might need bumpers on the crib more than another parent because we are worried about our cutie's BnB getting stuck in between the slats of the crib (it has happened to us). Or we might be more concerned about what they sleep in because we want to limit their access to their BnB in the hopes that they will not try to take them off during the night. So, we will buy all the swaddles and sleep sacks that will fit the BnB, just to delay the attempts to escape in the middle of the night (we certainly have). We might need to buy a better video monitor so that we can make sure our cutie can successfully roll over while in their BnB. Believe me it is tempting to think that a product will transform your cutie's sleep, but the reality is that there may not be an easy answer, and we will simply have to be patient with ourselves and our cuties.

HANDLING SKIN ISSUES

W HEN WE FIRST TRANSITIONED TO BnB, I doctored the boots up with moleskin in the heel, on the inside tongue of the boot, and at the top of the back of the boot. We also used the black robin socks and a pressure saddle. I was afraid of our cutie getting blisters, so I did all of this *before* she wore her boots the first time! In my attempt to prevent blisters, my modifications actually caused too much pressure on her heel and she developed pre-blister red spots.

Discussed Topics:

- Preventing blisters and red spots
  - o Important tips
- Items to purchase
- Other foot problems
  - o Ingrown toenails
  - o Athlete's Foot

Preventing Blisters and Red Spots

Red spots developed on our cutie's heels almost immediately. They were only on the back of her heels, but they did not go away until she decreased to 16-18 hour wear. Thankfully these spots never developed into blisters, but there were a couple of times when she was teetering right on the edge of blister town. An example of these red marks is in picture 8.1. I don't know why they developed. Maybe we had too much padding or bulk on the boot to prevent the blisters or maybe the first boots were too small and once the problem areas developed they never had the chance to properly heal. Whatever the reason, they were a constant source of worry for my husband and I, and we made at least one extra trip to the doctor to have them checked.

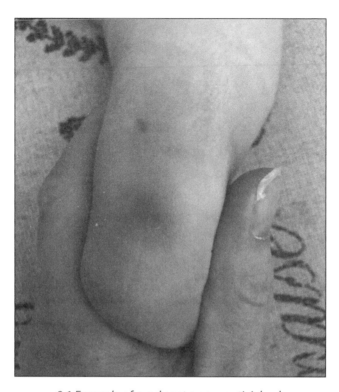

8.1 Example of a red spot on our cutie's heel.

What ended up working for us was taking all of the added bulk out of her boots. We removed the moleskin and pressure saddles. Picture 8.2 shows what we had in the boot and eventually removed. We also tried not to use any band aids on the heel itself. These measures seemed to put less pressure on the heel and helped alleviate some of the redness. It never went away fully, but it improved. If we noticed a red mark starting to develop, we would put a thin layer of Duoderm on the spot until it improved again. We also religiously used the Foot Glide blister prevention and put it on before each BnB wear. This helped if any other small red spots on the tops of the feet or in the crease of the big toe appeared.

There is a balancing act with the boots that no one really prepares you for. You want to make the middle strap (and the other straps, but especially the middle) tight enough to keep the heel down, but not so tight that it creates too much pressure, thus causing blisters or sores. It feels like a balancing act because you want to keep the foot, especially the heel, down and in the boot and the main way to do this is by tightening the middle strap. We ended up having to back off a notch on the middle strap to help with the redness, but we worried that it wasn't keeping her heel down enough. For more discussion about heel placement refer to the Boots and Bar section in Chapter 4.

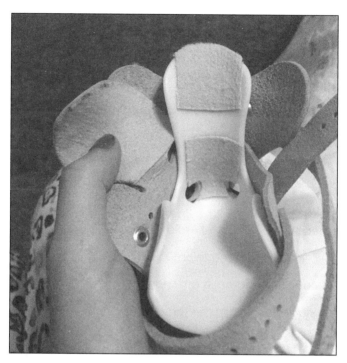

8.2 Picture of the moleskin we had placed inside the boot and eventually removed.

Important tips:

- If your cutie develops a blister, and they need to be out of their boots for it to heal, remember that relapse doesn't happen overnight. A day or two BnB-free will not cause your baby to lose any of their correction. Also, you'll want to allow the blister to fully heal to prevent infection.

- It's good to get in the habit of giving your cutie's skin a once-over immediately after removing the boots, to check for any red spots or swelling.

  o Any red spots that do not go away after 20 minutes of free time are most likely there to stay unless the issue is resolved.

o   In our experience, the red spots didn't cause any discomfort for our baby, but they didn't go away until we decreased to 18-hour wear. We did everything possible to prevent them from becoming blisters and in the end, we were successful, as they never became open sores.

Red spots can be caused by multiple factors:

- Your cutie has begun to outgrow their current boot size and it is causing friction.

- The tongue across the boot was not flush against the foot while buckled in and caused irritation during 23-hour wear.

- A wrinkle in the sock caused bunching and friction against the skin.

- The middle strap is too tight and is causing pressure on the foot (especially true if on the top of the foot).

- The boots are new, not worn in yet, and still stiff.

- Not enough padding in the shoe.

- Too much padding in the shoe (our issue).

Warning: Never use lotions on the feet, especially if there is a red spot. This will only make the issue worse. Instead, we used a body glide to soothe the soreness away.

Items to Buy

Here is a list of items that we purchased or were recommended to purchase for blister protection and prevention.

- Duoderm - Amazon - I was unable to find Duoderm at my local drugstore or grocery store, so we ordered it online. This worked well for our cutie and could be cut into small pieces to cover any red spots.

- BodyGlide Foot - Anti Blister Balm Amazon - We have 3 different sticks of BodyGlide one upstairs, one downstairs, and one in the diaper bag. This makes it convenient to have on hand whenever we are putting on the BnB.

- o   We put it on the heels, and on any spot that is red, such as the Big toe crease, top of the foot, middle strap with tongue.

- Moleskine – Amazon - This thin, soft material with sticky adhesive that can be used on the boots to provide comfort on pressure spots.

- Band-Aids – Hydro Seal Blister Heels- These band-aids work great on the back of the heel to protect or prevent blisters.

- Compeed- Advanced Blister Care bandages

- Bacitracin - Antibiotic Ointment - First Aid Antibiotic

  - o   Can be used on an open wound.

- Molefoam – A thicker padding that can be used to cushion and protect blisters and sores.

- Foam Facial Pads - A fellow clubfoot mom used this instead of a pressure saddle and had success.

- Baby Powder – You can put a shake or two inside your cutie's socks before putting them on. A small-sized bottle makes it easier to control the powder.

- Sheepskin - Walmart, Amazon, Craft Store. This can be glued to the top of the inside of the tongue or placed by a shoe cobbler.

  - o   For a good video on how to do it at home watch the videos on ClubHub and YouTube titled, "Applying Sheepskin to Mitchell Ponseti® boots."

- Coflex- Amazon 12 pack $11.99 - A sticky material to keep the heel in place

- Plastazote - Foam padding that can be used as padding in the boot.

- Hydrocolloidal Bandage - Made for open sores or burns and can be provided by a pharmacist

Other Foot Problems

While blisters and pressure sores are the major issues your cutie's skin will encounter during BnB, there are other foot problems that you might run into along the way, such as ingrown toenails and athletes' foot. A lot of kids with clubfoot have toenails will look different from a typical foot. If your cutie is anything like mine, her big toenail is curled up toward the sky, rather than pointing straight out. Her pinky toenails also look more like a triangle than a square, coming to a point at the top rather than flat across. The shape of the toenails can make them difficult to maintain by filing and trimming, so you may have to do something different than you would with typical toes.

I'm not going to lie and say that they look "normal," because frankly the first time I saw a clubfoot baby with toenails like this I thought it looked bizarre! I remember telling my husband if our babies toenails looked like that, I would call the doctor immediately because I didn't think it looked normal. But like most other clubfoot things, I had to adjust my idea of normal and looking back now I chuckle to myself about my reaction. Now her toenails look completely "clubfoot normal" to me, and I love them so much.

It is important to remember that your cutie is wearing shoes and socks much longer than typical children do because of the BnB. I equate it to wearing hiking boots for the same amount of time. Just like with hiking boots, you need to adjust to them when you get them and then if you wear them too long, issues are guaranteed to arise. You will have to consider the implications of what this type of "boot" wear will have on your cutie and be able to come up with some creative solutions.

Ingrown Toenails

An ingrown toenail is when the corner or side of a toenail (usually on the big toe) grows into the surrounding flesh. The ingrown toenail can cause redness, swelling, and pain and can even lead to an infection if not treated. My cutie has not experienced ingrown toenails, but it tends to be a common affliction for clubfoot cuties. Some of my fellow clubfoot moms have shared their experiences with ingrown toenails with me. You can also search archives in social media groups such as the Clubfoot Support group, to see how other parents helped their cutie's ingrown toenails.

Here are some ideas of how to help:

- Cut the toes of socks off to allow the toes to breathe and have better circulation.

  You may want to buy cheaper socks if you do this, such as Target or Walmart brand, because cutting the toes of expensive Black Robin or smart knit socks may not be your best option.

- Keep the toenails slightly longer but still straight across. Ingrown toenails develop more readily if their nail is curved and cut too short, so keep the nails long and square when possible.

- We use the Fridababy nail kit, which includes, an S-shaped nail file and nail clippers. These have worked well for us. I usually don't have to clip my cutie's nails, but find filing is more effective. The S-shaped file seems to work well with her curved toenails.

- If you think there is an infection, contact a medical professional who can prescribe antibiotic ointment that can be applied.

- If you have any major concerns or the ingrown toenail is happening frequently, contact your medical professional for help on how to proceed.

Athletes Foot

This fungal infection can be caused when sweaty feet are confined within tight fitting shoes or boots. Our cutie has experienced athletes' foot once so far in her BnB journey. This is common for many cuties. Additionally, when your cutie starts to walk and is wearing shoes much of the day, as well as their BnB during sleep, this can cause extra sweating and lead to athlete's foot. Here are some remedies that other parents have found helpful and that their doctors have recommended. Of course, if you are concerned, contacting your doctor is always your best bet. If your clubfoot doctor is not available, you can always contact your pediatrician. Just remember to provide a gentle reminder that the issue is exacerbated by BnB wear. Here are some products that can be helpful:

- Lotrimin - Purchased at local grocery store or amazon or target

- o   Lotrimin applied twice a day was our doctor's recommendation and the course of treatment that worked for us.

- o   I put the Lotrimin on before her BnB and then after we took them off. Our cutie was in night and nap wear, so this was about 4 times per day. It cleared up within 5 days.

- Baby powder in the socks at night (some say this can lock in more moisture so check with your doctor before trying)

- Pure Fractionated Coconut oil with a few drops of lavender oil - Apply twice a day.

  Ask your pediatrician to prescribe a medicated ointment if necessary and ask about oral antifungal prescription if ointments are not clearing it up. You can also consider the following strategies

- Switch to cotton or bamboo socks to help prevent excessive sweating.

- Wear socks when wearing walking shoes.

  Before the Athletes foot, our cutie was wearing her shoes without socks. When it cleared up, we had her wear socks with her shoes always to prevent extra sweating directly in the shoes.

- Keep bare feet as much as possible around the house.

- Avoid putting any slipper type shoe or boot on her in order to prevent excessive sweating.

When your cutie is in BnB, especially during the initial 23-hour wear, you are desperate to make them as comfortable as possible, and the addition of skin issues can complicate things. Skin issues add another layer of stress to an already stressful situation. Trying to figure out the best way to help your cutie can feel daunting. I felt so much stress about my cutie's red spots during BnB, and it seemed like nothing I tried helped. I was frustrated and anxious and desperate to find a way to alleviate the red spots, but in the end our physical therapist reminded us that it is about her comfort.

When we took her to the physical therapist to assess the red spots and discuss different options to help, he pressed directly on the red spots and told us to watch her reaction. She didn't react. She didn't seem to notice it at all and realizing that the spots were not causing her direct discomfort helped my anxiety tremendously. It reminded me that while I was focused on finding solutions for her skin issues, I also needed to watch her for signs of discomfort.

When our cutie transitioned to BnB, we checked her feet regularly to ensure that there were no developing issues with her skin. We would take her boot off and examine her entire foot, front and back, and assess if there were any emergent issues. The majority of the time her foot was red in one section or another simply due the placement of her foot in the boot, but the redness would go away within minutes (other than the red spots on the backs of her heels). If the redness persisted after 15 minutes out of the boot, it was an indication that there was something we would need to keep our eye on. It is great to get in the habit of looking at your cutie's feet right when they come out of the boots, so that you are aware if there are any changes in the skin that you want to keep an eye on. My husband loves to give our cuties feet a little rub when he takes her BnB off in the morning, and it is great opportunity to give those little feet some extra love and attention.

CHAPTER 9

PRACTICAL IMPACTS
OF BnB

Y OU HAVE READ ABOUT THE initial transition to BnB and looked at various schedules for moving forward, but there are other areas in which the BnB will impact your daily care of your cutie. In this chapter, I discuss several areas in which our daughter's direct care was impacted by the BnB and will provide suggestions that worked for us. Also included are product recommendations that you may find helpful.

Discussed Topics:

- Breastfeeding
- Babywearing
- Traveling
- Financial
- Travel and other recommendations

Breastfeeding in BnB

If you just came off casting and you thought *that* made for awkward nursing, I'm here to tell you it gets more cumbersome when your cutie's feet are tethered together. My cutie and I had a rough go of breastfeeding in general, but it was so important to me that we push through and make it work because I wanted to be able to provide her comfort in this way throughout all of her treatments. We worked through it during casting and eventually found our rhythm. We probably hit our stride right when transitioning to BnB, when she was a little over 2 months old. We had found a latch that worked and as she got bigger, she adjusted to my milk flow better, and then we had to start BnB. In all honesty, it was probably good that the transition happened when it did because we had worked through so many kinks already that the BnB seemed like just another kink to work through.

We settled on the sideways nursing hold, with her legs draped across my body. It seemed to be the most comfortable for us. That way the BnB could lay below her head and there was plenty of room to rest them across my lap. It becomes a little more cumbersome when switching sides because you have an extra piece that you need to watch out for. This was especially true during night feedings. Be careful that you don't hit yourself with the boots (the bar will probably be covered, but the boots can really leave a mark if they come down hard). Your baby will still want to move their feet and that means that the BnB will move with it.

I would use the night nursing sessions to check her heel placement in the boots by placing my pinky finger inside the heel hole and seeing if I could feel her heel. If I could feel most of it I knew it was okay. If I couldn't feel anything, or just barely the top, we would readjust the boots. It worked best when her feet were below, but as she got bigger sometimes the bar was hard to keep below or even fit in the rocking chair. Nursing in bed was easier except for the 50 pillows I needed to prop us up. We never did the lying-down side nursing in bed, but other clubfoot mammas said that it was successful for them. You just need to make sure that you don't get whacked in the face with the bar when your baby lifts their feet up. Nursing in the rocking chair was less comfortable but became necessary when she moved to her own room.

Babywearing in BnB

When I was pregnant with my cutie I had grand plans to carry her in a baby carrier wherever we went. I did research on the best carriers for clubfoot cutie's in both the casting and BnB phases of treatment. I ended up purchasing a rather expensive carrier, however much like many other aspects of clubfoot treatment, my expectations did not meet my reality. My cutie hated the carrier, the wrap, and any other contraption I tried to attach to my body that would allow me to carry her hands free. Don't get me wrong, she insisted on being held at all times of the day, but screamed incessantly whenever I tried to put her in a carrier. I was even desperate enough to buy a second, and equally expensive, carrier in hopes for more success, with no luck! I also tried the Moby wrap when she was in casting and she despised that as well.

I realize that babywearing was more complicated because of my anxiety about wanting to ensure her hips and legs were supported accurately which probably took a bit of practice. My middle daughter loved being in the carrier and I would strap her on and we would head out to whatever activity we were off too. I wanted to experience the same thing with my cutie. I knew a carrier would have made my life simpler because it would have allowed me to have my hands free to do even simple things like make dinner. Not to mention how the carrier would have decreased the bodily toll it took on me hold her in one arm all the time. We just never seemed to get the hang of it. I don't know whether it was my own self-doubt in properly getting her into the carrier or her extreme will to fight against it, that made me give up trying but eventually I threw in the towel. I let go of the expectation and accepted the reality that it just wasn't going to work for us.

I don't want my experience to deter you from trying it with your cutie. I know other clubfoot mommas who had great success wearing their cuties and there is an entire Facebook group dedicated to support you carrying your cutie called Babywearing for Clubfoot Babies. This is an amazing resource that provides how-to videos, suggestions on correct positions in the carrier, and recommendations on which carriers work best for cuties. If you are interested in trying to carry your cutie, I would definitely check them out.

Here are some suggestions for your babywearing journey.

- Try to borrow a carrier before you buy- Learn from my experience and try to borrow a carrier before you purchase one, that way if it doesn't work you do not have to deal with the hassle of trying to return it.

- Look for a gently used carrier- Sometimes you can purchase a carrier in good condition from another mom, which can you save you money. Since the carriers are used for only a year or two, much like other baby items, they are ripe for being reused. I have seen carriers for resale on Babywearing for Clubfoot Babies.

- Ask questions about positioning- If you are concerned about your baby's hips or knee placement in the carrier you can ask your medical provider or an experienced clubfoot mom's advice. It may take some practice to get your cutie into the right position, rather than give up like I did, ask someone else for some help, it could be a gamechanger.

- Be flexible- Much like any other aspect of clubfoot treatment, you will need to approach babywearing with some flexibility. You should follow you and your cutie's lead and do what works best for both of you. If your cutie hates the carrier after several tries, maybe take a break from trying and come back to it later. If your cutie loves it but your back kills while wearing it, maybe adjust the settings on the carrier or try a different carrier.

Product recommendations:

Here are the carriers I purchased, plus a couple more that have been recommended through the clubfoot community.

- Becca Gemini Cool Mesh, Sleek and Simple 5-in-1 Carrier- Amazon $90-

    I purchased this as my second carrier, hoping that the simpler design would assist my cutie and I in finding a comfortable position. It didn't work out for us, but I do think the design is simpler and the mesh aspect of the design definitely provides a cooling effect. The price varies on Amazon, so I watched and waited until the price dropped before purchasing.

- Lillebaby Complete All Seasons- Lillebaby website, Amazon, Target- $80-120

    This was the first carrier I purchased and has several options for positioning. It is sturdy and provides a lot of support for both you and baby. I did have some difficulty figuring out the base width, as it is adjustable for a wider and smaller base, and never seemed to find the right fit. There are so many people who love this carrier though, clubfoot and non-clubfoot mommas alike.

- Moby Classic Baby Wrap- Target $40

    I purchased this during the casting phase because my best friends' baby literally lived in it, so I thought maybe I could figure out how to make it work for my cutie too. I think we successfully used it once, where I felt like her hips and legs were supported adequately and she didn't scream the entire time. I eventually returned it because we just didn't use it enough to make it worth it, but I have seen clubfoot moms have great success with wraps during both phases of treatment so it might be worth a try for you and your cutie.

- Ergo 360 Baby Carrier, All Carry Positions- Amazon, Target $119

  This carrier was recommended by a fellow clubfoot mom who said that her cutie enjoyed being in it. It is another carrier that is recommended in the Facebook group as a good choice for clubfoot cuties.

- Baby Bjorn New Baby Carrier One Air- Amazon, $219

  This was a carrier that was recommended by other clubfoot moms in the Facebook group. It looks super sturdy and great for stability but seems more expensive than the other recommended carriers.

Traveling with BnB

Most likely you and your cutie will have to do some sort of traveling while in the first year of BnB wear, and it can be overwhelming trying to prepare for travel during this stage. Whether you are traveling for treatment or pleasure, it's good to have a plan in place. Let's face it, traveling with infants is a lot of work in and of itself. How can such little people have so much stuff? You will most likely have a stroller and car seat system for travel, as well as all the diaper bag and supplies.

We had to fly with our cutie during her 23-hour BnB wear for treatment reasons. For us, the biggest hurdle during travel was going through security. The first time my husband and I did it, I walked through security holding her with her BnB on. Of course, the alarms went off and I ended up having a pat down for security purposes. I didn't want to take her BnB off because it would have been a hassle to get them back on in the chaos of the security area while still making it to our gate on time. It also would have used up her 20 minutes of free time, which I was banking for later. We wanted to put a blanket down at the gate area to let her have free time before we boarded the plane instead.

Our stroller folded down to fit through the security and we put the car seat through as well. If you are traveling solo, I recommend leaving your baby in the car seat until you have everything else (stroller, bags, jacket, shoes, and etc.) on the conveyer belt to be x-rayed. Then you can take your baby out and put the car seat on the conveyer belt as well. It has been my experience that people are helpful, patient, and understanding when you are traveling solo with an infant. This is especially true with a baby who has a strange looking device strapped to their feet, so don't feel rushed or like you're holding up the security line. You are prepared and have a plan, and everyone else will most likely be kind and understanding!

Once all of your gear is on the conveyer belt, you'll walk through security holding your baby, and then reverse the order as you collect your things. Put your cutie in the car seat first and then get the rest of your belongings. On our return flight, I decided to leave our cutie's boots on, but removed the bar and sent it through the security with the jackets and shoes. When I did this, I didn't have to get any extra security checks. If you don't want to remove the entire BnB, then just pop only the bar off. The bulk of the metal is on the bar anyway, and if they make you go through extra security, well hey, it was worth a shot!

When my cutie turned nine months old, I made the decision to designate the plane as a "boot-free zone." Even if she needed to sleep, I reasoned it was okay for her to sleep on the plane without the BnB. This works for us because our flights are typically short, and we don't travel often. If you are traveling frequently, this policy may not be the best practice for your cutie. For us, when she had decreased to the 14-16 hour stage we were generally flying without my husband. I made the decision that it was hard enough to fly solo without having to worry about the cumbersome BnB. It made sleeping on the plane just a tad easier and I didn't have to worry about the BnB hitting the person sitting next to us. As we continue to travel with our cutie, the plane will remain a boot-free zone, unless extreme circumstances (such as a long international flight) dictate otherwise. We generally make up the BnB hours we missed on the plane by putting her BnB on directly after the flight. We usually have extra travel time in the car after our flight, so it's easy to make up the time when she's in her car seat. We will continue to be traveling solo together for her treatment, and this will be the plan moving forward, but I will try to remind myself, and subsequently remind you, to remain flexible when traveling. Traveling with children is difficult enough, and just like other areas of life, the BnB adds another layer of complexity to the situation. So, remember to take a deep breath and be brave. You can do this, and you will find a groove much like you have in all the other aspects of BnB!

When your baby is in 23-hour wear and traveling, managing the schedule can be difficult between free time and BnB wear. We decided to do free time at the gates while waiting to get on the plane, do stretches, and put the BnB back on before we got on the plane. It made for an unhappy baby most of the flight and the changing on the plane more than cumbersome, but it was better than trying to get the BnB on and off while on the jam-packed plane. Our cutie was a very cranky flyer at this time in her life and the flights consisted of lots of knee bouncing, rattle shaking, and ABC singing in order to keep her semi-calm. She was also a finicky sleeper, and we made the mistake of sitting in the aisle, which inevitably meant that anytime someone walked by it would startle her awake. Therefore, the next time we flew we chose the window seat where we were more tucked away. While it was not great for diaper changes, it provided a more successful nap time.

I think bringing a new toy, lots of snacks, and little things to fiddle with are the best ways to distract and keep your cutie (and truly, any baby!) busy while on a plane. Nursing my cutie during the flights helped to calm and soothe her to sleep. For those of you who bottle-feed, remember to build in time for TSA to check your milk or formula before the flight. If you are anything like me, it helps to try and plan for the worst-case scenario and then work back from there. That way I'm pleasantly surprised when things don't completely fall apart and consider it a win when only a few missteps happen.

Like many people, I'm not great about asking for help. I don't do it well in my everyday life, and it certainly isn't in my nature to seek out help when traveling. A fellow clubfoot mom reminded me that people are often friendly and to not be afraid to ask for help when you need it. Approaching a stranger and asking for help is a bit too far out of my comfort zone. But my friend's gentle reminder helped me make the decision that if someone offered help, I could say yes if I needed it.

A man sitting next to me on the plane asked if he could get my bags down from the overhead bin and instead of saying, "It's okay, I can do it," I said "yes, thank you!" When someone asks, "can I help you?" it feels a bit open-ended. It can be overwhelming to verbalize exactly what you need in that moment! When someone asked something specific, like "Can I hold something for you?" then it's easier for me to accept the help offered.

Once, while riding a train, a woman offered her seat to me as I was struggling to keep the stroller close. Instead of declining her offer, I said, "Yes, please and thank you!" I didn't feel guilty about my response or that she gave up her seat, because she offered the help and I was happy to accept it. I remind myself that saying please and thank you go a long way in the gratefulness department, plus it often makes people feel good when you accept their help.

Items to carry on the plane:

- Baby wipes

- 5-7 diapers – A must for all travel

- Baby blanket - Muslin or thin blanket- that can be put down as a changing table or on a changing table in a pinch

- Diaper cream - We use Vaniply

- Tylenol - Infant with a syringe

- Band Aids - Blister ones

- New toy – Try a book, something age appropriate that baby has never seen before

- Snacks - Puffs, yogurt melts, teething crackers, baked puffs (Cheeto type). I stayed away from bars or anything that would make a crumbly mess.

- 2 Burp cloths - Can be multipurpose

- Sippy cup - Fill with water before getting on the plane

- Two extra pairs of clothes - I like onesie and pants, separates, so if one got dirty or wet, then I could switch out just one rather than the whole outfit.

- Extra pair of socks - Whichever ones your cuties wear with their BnB

- Extra shirt for yourself - In case of puke or spit up

- Headphones

- Gum

- Extra contacts - Glasses

- Phone charger

- Birth Certificate or immunization records to verify baby's age

- BnB - Always pack in carry on, even if checking bags so that you do not have to stress if your luggage gets lost

- Doggie poop bags- For dirty diapers. They are easy to store and use anywhere.

- Stroller and Car Seat - We have the Chicco Keyfit Stroller and car seat system. It worked well for travel as both the stroller and the car seat will fit through the security belt. The one piece of advice I have is, if you are using it as a combined system with car seat attached, when you gate check it, make sure you detach the snack tray and bring it on the plane with you. The snack tray is what makes the car seat fit into the stroller, and if it breaks during transit, you will be in trouble when you get to your destination.

- Duoderm

We chose to gate check the stroller and car seat when our cutie was an infant, rather than check it as luggage. This made it easier to maneuver the airport and carry all our gear. When gate checking the stroller and car seat, you have to get gate tags for both when you arrive at the gate. Some other friends chose to bring the stroller and check the car seat. This is what we did when our daughter moved out of her bucket car seat, but when she was in the bucket, we chose to bring it because she tended to nap better in it than in the stroller itself. It was worth the extra piece of equipment if I knew she would sleep in it. Some friends who traveled frequently bought separate strollers and car seats just for traveling, that way if something broke, they wouldn't be upset.

Travel and Other Product Recommendations

Below is a list of the stroller and car seat recommendations that we had direct experience with. You can also find other product recommendations on the following websites: Clubfoot CARES, the Clubfoot Store, and the clubfoothub.

Here are some car seat and stroller options to consider:

- *Car seat and Stroller* - Chicco Bravo Trio Travel System- Amazon - This is a stroller, base and car seat. During the casting phase we used a Britax car seat, which worked fine but when we transitioned to BnB the base of the car seat was too small and it did not accommodate the BnB, even in the bar's smallest setting. The BnB had to rest completely on top of the bottom of the car seat or at least one boot had to be all the way up on one side. It did not seem safe or supportive and I needed a car seat that could accommodate her BnB better, because she was going to be in it a lot. We measured the BnB end to end to get the largest width and I went to Target to measure the base of several different car seats recommended and the only on that measured close was the Chicco Bravo.

  o For convenience, I wanted a bucket seat that could go from car seat to stroller for pick up and drop off especially. The base of the Chicco was still not a perfect fit, but provided substantially more room than the Britax did.

  o We would roll up a receiving blanket or muslin blanket and tuck it under ankles to prop it up and provide support. This evened out the BnB too, so one side wasn't sitting higher than another.

  o During cold weather we would wrap her in a blanket in the car seat. I would tuck half the blanket under her BnB and use the rest to cover her bottom half. I used this stroller/car seat system about 3-4 times a day, so it was worth it to me. I wish I would have had the foresight to buy this system originally.

- *One-year Car seat* - Graco 4 ever All-in-One Convertible Car seat Target - We purchased this car seat for our cutie and started using it when she was about 13 months old. I used my car seat trade in coupon at Target to purchase this car seat and saved about $60.

  o A friend recommended this car seat and we liked the idea of it because it changes to a high back booster and regular booster as your child grows.

  o It fits into our minivan, in the rear facing position, easily (which was a problem with other car seats we had tried with our older girls). We didn't research the width to accommodate the BnB as we did with the bucket car seat, because at the time that she would be using it, she would not have her BnB on as often. When she did need to wear her BnB (on road trips mainly) it fit easily and did not seem to cause any discomfort.

- *Go by Goldbug Dual Facing Mirror* – Target - I purchased this mirror when my daughter transitioned to 14-16 hour BnB wear solely for the purpose of seeing if she was trying to fall asleep in the car. Up until this point whenever my daughter was in the car seat her BnB was on. Once she transitioned to fewer hours of wear, she didn't wear them as often. At this point, the struggle became keeping her awake in the car so she didn't begin to associate sleep without wearing the BnB. This mirror became key in quickly seeing if she was getting drowsy and I would turn on her favorite music and jam out on the way home. As she got older, the mirror became useful when I wanted her to take a quick catnap in the car and would alert her sisters to be quiet when she was sleeping. A great buy for travel reasons in particular.

I wanted to include some of the toy items we bought specifically for our cutie to help with her development. As your cutie grows, as with any other baby, you will want to have items that can help their physical and mental growth. This list consists of items that we purchased to help with her physical development.

- *Piano Playmate* - Amazon - Fisher Price Deluxe Kick and Play - We bought this when our daughter first transitioned to BnB to use during the free time segments to encourage her to kick her feet. This toy played adorable songs that we still sing to her today, and she remembers them.

  o I particularly liked this toy because it has a removable bar with toys hanging below, so she could explore with both hands and feet. When she got too big for it, we were able to remove the piano, and she can play with that separately on her own now. This toy has had longevity for us. She still played with it after she turned one.

- *Fisher-Price Little People Music Parade Ride-On* – Target - We bought this car/push toy for our cutie for her first birthday to encourage her walking. The handle in the back makes this car easy for parents and kids to navigate.

  o Our cutie loved this car and spent hours being pushed around or pushing her sisters around on it.

- *VTech Sit-to-Stand Learning Walker* - Amazon - We started using this with our cutie around 9-10 months to encourage pulling up and walking. Our cutie took her first assisted steps while using this product (while the whole family cheered her on). It has a locking system so you can lock one or both wheels at two different settings, which allows you more control over how easy or difficult it is to push. We used both locks on full force at first to help stabilize her as she pulled herself up and then lessened the locks as she grew more confident in her walking. The front detaches so you can take it off and let your cutie play with it while they are still in the sitting/crawling phase.

This is the high chair that we purchased and how it worked for us:

- *Highchair - Grace Blossom 6-in-1 Seating System Convertible Highchair* - Target - All three of our daughter's used this highchair, though we purchased a new one for our cutie. We started using it frequently around 6 months. We used the car seat trade in program from Target to purchase this highchair. This program applies to many baby items, not just car seats!

- o This highchair worked great with the BnB because the entire tray comes off easily in one movement. You can strap your cutie in while in their BnB and easily slide the tray back on.

- o There are three different trays in one spot, so if the top tray gets dirty you can detach it and clean it, and still have two backups to use if needed. We liked the extra padding in the seat for when our cutie was smaller as it provided more support and security for her while sitting.

Financial Impacts

Any medical treatment is going to directly impact you and your family's financial situation. Clubfoot treatment can be expensive, and depending on your health insurance coverage, it can cause a financial burden for your family. Since we knew about our cutie's diagnosis before she was born, we were able to spend time trying to figure out how much her casting treatment was going to cost, but we were still surprised by the total amount. I am of the mindset that the more prepared you can be for a situation, the better you are able to manage it while going through it. I planned for us to meet our total out of pocket deductible for the year, then when we did, I wasn't upset about the amount of money we spent. We were able to plan accordingly, like we skipped the family vacation that year, to make sure we were prepared for the cost.

I realize that we are lucky to have health insurance and the financial means to pay for all of her treatment without placing a terrible burden on our family. Not everyone is the same situation as we are, and you may need to look into financial resources to help you and your family. Betsy Miller's "A Parent's Guide to Clubfoot" has a great list of places that can help with financial assistance for treatment including the Ponseti International Association, Shriners Hospitals for Children, Air and Ground transportations (to help you get to the doctor you need), and Ronald McDonald House (to provide housing if you are traveling for treatment) (2012 p.25-26). Dr.

Dobbs and his team also try to provide financial assistance to families in need and can help you if you choose to receive treatment in St. Louis. If you need financial assistance, please research and inquire about it with your medical team or another doctor if necessary.

When you enter the BnB phase of treatment, the majority of the financial impact will be purchasing the boots and bar, and any necessary accessories. There are resources to help with these items such as the Clubfoot Boot Exchange Program through the Clubfoot Cares Website. You can complete an application for donated boots on their page, and if you qualify they will provide you with free boots (https://www.clubfootcares.org/application-for-donated-boots). They do not provide the bars, only the boots at this time. I know that when we ordered bar covers from 26th Ave Clubfoot Essentials there was an option to donate money to help provide bar covers, so if you are unable to afford a bar and would like one, I suggest you contact them and see how their donation process works. There are resources out there, you may need to search a little further for them.

CHAPTER 10

RELATIONAL IMPACTS
OF BnB

THE LAST CHAPTER FOCUSED ON the logistical and practical impacts that the BnB will have on you and your cutie's life, but this chapter will focus on another significant impact of BnB which is relationships. During that first year of treatment, it can feel like every relationship you have — whether it be with family, friends, acquaintances, or simply passersby — will be impacted by your child's clubfoot treatment. Of course, there are the big relationships like those with your other children or with your domestic partner, but there are also the quick interactions with people you briefly encounter that will be impacted by your child's BnB. This chapter is meant to help you take time and focus on these relationships and interactions with some forethought before you are thrust into the chaos that BnB treatment can bring.

Partner Relationship

If you are going through your cutie's clubfoot treatment with a partner, it will certainly have an impact on your relationship. As I have alluded to throughout this book my husband and I tend to approach the world from different perspectives and sometimes these differences complement each other and sometimes they contradict each other. The journey through our cutie's clubfoot treatment provided both opportunities to compliment and contradict each other, and you may find yourself and your partner in a similar situation.

To understand our relationship dynamic, you need to know that my husband and I are high school sweethearts, meaning we essentially grew up together. He is by far my favorite person on the planet and I rarely get tired of being with him. He is easy going, positive, kind, loving and persistent. I am anxious, realistic, emotional, direct, and opinionated. We work together really well most of the time, but when we go off track, we tend to really veer off track.

One of the things I believe we do best is we both have the ability to let the other take the lead when it suits their strength. When it came to choosing a doctor, making the decision to switch doctors, and the over-all understanding of the clubfoot treatment, my husband let me take the lead. As you can tell by this book, I am a researcher. I am a knowledge seeker, a reader, and learner and when it came to be preparing for our cutie's treatment these were my strengths. My husband supported me throughout and provided insight when needed but largely followed my lead in this aspect of treatment. It worked for us because if we both tried to take charge it could have led to discord and confusion, and we des-perately needed a clear path forward amidst all of the confusion we were already experiencing. I suggest that you and your partner take some time after your cutie's original diagnosis to discuss your strengths and deter-mine who would be best to take the lead in which portions of treatment.

I realize that not everyone reading this book has a master's in therapy and may not be as eager to take a hard look at yourself and your partner's strengths and weaknesses, but I think if you make a commitment to at least try it can make a big difference in how you will handle the emotional and physical toll that the clubfoot journey will take on your relationship. Be careful to keep this conversation authentic and validating. By authen-tic I mean you have to be honest with yourself about your weaknesses as well as your partner's. This is not a conversation where you are placing blame or looking for faults in your partner, but to honestly discuss your fears and concerns. That is where the validating will come in. You have to be able to listen to your partner's experience and validate how they are feeling without judgement, and vice versa.

You can even make this conversation about the positives if you are afraid that bringing up weakness will be too difficult or distracting. Focus on what each of you are best at and then talk about a game plan for how you can each support the other during treatment. But if you can dive a little deeper, and openly discuss your fear in a safe environment, I truly believe there is such a beauty and growth in those conversations.

Obviously having a therapist for a wife meant that my husband knew what was in store for him in the conversation department. That doesn't mean that it is comfortable for him. I know that these conversations push his comfort zone and he can struggle tapping into his deep emotions. I am much more comfortable discussing my deeper emotions (probably too comfortable if you ask him), and this is another way we can complement each other. I can get caught up in all my anxiety and fear and have a difficult time seeing outside of it, and my husband is usually able to pull me out and ground me in the present. During the two months between when we finished casting and had our appointment with Dr. Dobbs, there were several times that I fell victim to the "What if?" What if her feet are not corrected? What if we have to redo treatment all over again? What if I have to stay alone in a new city for treatment with an infant?

It was always my husband who would bring me back to now by asking what I really thought when I looked at her feet. The truth was I never really thought that there was an issue with her feet, but my anxiety caused the self-doubt. He was able to calm me down by bringing me back to the present, what was true right now. Because he doesn't tap into his anxiety as frequently and readily as I do, he was able to support me emotionally by grounding me. It was a complimentary strength to one of my weaknesses that allowed him to take the lead and help move us forward in treatment. It was also so important that he provided a safe place for me to explore these emotions without judgement. He never diminished my feelings or told me that I was stupid for feeling that way. He validated me and supported me (who is the therapist now, right?).

When you embark on the clubfoot journey together it is not only an emotional but a systematic challenge as well. By system, I mean a family and a couple system (a unit). In a relationship we tend to play our parts, we have our roles and we do them in order to keep our system functioning. The leader, the supporter, the rock, the emotional one, the breadwinner, the caretaker. As I alluded to earlier, while we tend to fall into the specific roles in our own relationships, it is vital that there be flexibility in those roles. Clubfoot treatment found me struggling in this department, especially on this journey because I really tried to power through and be in charge of everything I could. I pushed myself into the leadership role and wouldn't allow my husband to help enough. I would definitely discuss with him but in the end, I saw all the decision making as my own. My husband also did not assert himself into the leadership role and push me to take some control, but in the end, I was responsible for the burn-out and resentment that I felt during treatment because I never had a hard conversation with him about how I was feeling.

When my cutie was born, we made the decision for me to stay at home full time (previously I was working part time with my older 2 girls). In what felt like a moment, I was thrust into a job I wasn't confident in (full time motherhood) and lost a lot of my self-identity, all while taking on a new burden of becoming my child's medical provider. It threw me for a major loop and in my efforts to try and do everything just right, I placed all the burden on myself to be her primary caretaker and make all her medical decisions. Well I am guessing you can figure out how long it took for me to feel burnt out and resentful that while my life had dramatically changed with our daughter's clubfoot treatment, his day to day life looked mainly the same. He still went into work every day and had his sense of purpose and self-identity. The disclaimer is that this is how I saw it but was not how he was actually experiencing it (he was struggling at work and to find an outlet for his emotions).

So, in my efforts to everything myself, and take a leadership role, I ended up resenting my partner. Why did my life change so much while his seemingly stayed the same? Why did I have to give up a job that I loved to care for my child? Why was I responsible for all the medical research, appointments, travel, logistics and he wasn't? But I had never asked for help, so how was he expected to know I needed it? I was too rigid in the role I had taken over and didn't allow the flexibility for him to step in and help. For the day to day stuff, when we were both home, I had no problem allowing him to take over and help with all necessary aspects of treatment, like stretches, BnB on, bedtime, frequent night wake-ups, constant holding and rocking. I was able to let him help with it all. But it was the big-time life stuff that I was unable to allow him to support me in. I wouldn't allow him to help me but then was mad at him for not helping. A winning situation, right? No! It certainly put strain on our relationship and caused some conflict between us. We weren't communicating openly with each other and we were stuck in the day to day struggle and lost track of the big picture.

You might find you and your partner experiencing a similar struggle. The daily BnB schedule alone is daunting and exhausting, and so much of your focus is on keeping your precious cutie as comfortable as possible, that it is easy to forget to check in with each other. It is easy to take your frustration out on your partner, because it feels unfair to direct it at the baby who is already going through so much. But I did feel frustrated and angry that my baby had to figure out the BnB and it was easy to direct that at my husband. He was the only other adult in the house, so he was the only logical choice. It was easy to direct my resentment at him, even though my cutie's diagnosis had been the crux that changed the course of my life, at least for the next few years. I struggled with displaced anger and unwittingly took that out on the person I was closest to.

We didn't purposefully miss each other, but over the course of a trying year with very little sleep it naturally happened. In the end we had tough conversations and we tried new ways to support each other. I let go of some control, allowed him in more, and he opened up about the emotional toll the difficult year had taken on him. We didn't work it all out, we are nowhere close to perfect, but we are committed to growing together and tackling any future challenges we may face.

Suggestions:

- Communicate- Be brave and be vulnerable with each other. Open up about your fears and misplaced emotions.

- Validate- Listen to each other and then validate each other's emotions.

- Provide a safe space- Listen without judgement to your partner, allow them to vent or express concern without shutting them down.

- Be flexible- recognize when something isn't working and be open to changing up the dynamic.

- Focus on strengths - Talk about each other's strengths and express gratitude for what you both bring to the table.

Navigating parenting as a couple is difficult enough without the added stress of a baby with medical needs. There are moments where you will undoubtedly snap at your partner. You are under a ton of pressure trying to care for your cutie and keep their feet in the correct position. You may break down and have moments that you are not proud of. One of our rules as a couple was what we argued about in the middle of night (like whose turn it was to get up) was not reopened in the light of day. Some things you will need to let slide and use whatever patience and grace you have left to forgive, forget, and move on. Remember that you are in this together. You made this child together and if you are still in a relationship then you will need to put in some work to focus on your relationship. It is important, because when you look up after a difficult year, they will be the person who is there sitting next to you.

The one thing you will need to be on the same page about consistently is persistent BnB wear. If either your partner or you have a different approach to BnB wear that is fine, but the mentality that the BnB is a must and not an option must be obtained by both of you. Thankfully my husband and I both had a strict mentality about our cutie's BnB wear from the beginning. We both knew that if we allowed breaks in wear for anything other than a medical need, it would be a slippery slope for all of us. It is best to have an upfront and direct conversation about BnB wear and if your opinions differ than you should consult with your doctor about the best approach and agree to follow their directive. It is important to remember that it is not a battle of who is right or wrong, but what is the best decision for your cutie. Make a firm decision together, or follow your doctor's lead and stick with it together. You will be stronger as a team that is there to support each other and your cutie on their clubfoot journey.

Siblings

As I have mentioned, our cutie has two older sisters, and their lives were also directly impacted by having a sister born with clubfoot. When our cutie was diagnosed in utero, the girls were five and three years old, and we had to figure out a way to explain her diagnosis to them. I remember feeling very overwhelmed and anxious about sharing the news with the girls because I felt so confused about the diagnosis myself. How was I supposed to explain to these young girls something that I didn't even have a true grasp on myself?

I could have chosen to not tell them and waited until our baby was born to let them know, and that might be the decision that you make, but I felt a very strong pull to be forthright with them immediately. When they didn't know, for about a week between initial diagnosis and when it was confirmed in another ultrasound, I felt like I was keeping something from them. They were witnessing my strong emotions about the diagnosis but didn't understand what they were about. Once the diagnosis was confirmed, and we had an idea of the treatment ahead, I wanted to nor-malize it for myself and for them too.

We chose to sit down and tell our daughters directly about the special thing their baby sister was going to be born with and how we were going to help her through treatment. We simply explained what clubfoot meant and how it was treated and then let them ask whatever questions they had about it. We answered all of their questions to the best of our knowl-edge and were honest when we didn't know the answer. We made sure that we focused on the fact that this was something that was fixable and that their sister would be able to do all the things they are able to do too.

We also asked for their help when she was born and emphasized that we were doing this as a family, and everyone would be a part of it. This is huge for my girls, because they are helpers (especially my eldest), and they desperately want to feel like they are part of any situation. After we told our daughters about the diagnosis, they would tell whoever asked about the baby that there was something special about our baby, that she would be born with clubfeet! My eldest would talk to the baby in my belly and tell her, "Don't worry baby, we will help you straighten your feet, and you will be great!"

When their sister was born, they loved her curved little feet so much. Since they already knew what the treatment was going to look like, they were not surprised by the casts or the BnB. We let them decorate her casts and help pick out which leg warmers she should wear that day. They were amazing helpers, and they loved their baby sister with intense force, but that didn't mean that they were immune to the impact that her intense medical care would have. Our cutie took a ton of our attention, and we were extra protective of her, which caused some issues with our girls.

We had to make sure that they held her carefully and that they didn't get her casts wet. They had to spend a block of time away from the swim-ming pool during summer because we couldn't risk her casts getting wet. If I am being truly honest, we spent the majority of that summer at home, inside, with far too much screen time. I was holding our cutie every time she slept, which meant that I was on the couch, and not able to play or help them get snacks during that time. It was a huge effort to even get them to any summer sport they were signed up for, like golf or swim les-sons due to the intensity for the transition to BnB.

I thought that once our cutie was in BnB things would get easier. We could go to the pool without worrying about the water, but it actually became more intense because she was so fussy during this time. It seemed that nothing would calm her down except bouncing endlessly on the exercise ball, so we spent so much time at home. When we tried to go places, like the zoo or park, their baby sister would inevitably have a meltdown, and we would have to head for home. It felt like the longest summer ever! I know that they struggled with the transition of having a fully attentive mom to a super distracted and anxious one. They continued to try and help whenever they could, like getting her BnB stuff for me or playing with her during her 20 minutes of free time, but I saw their frustration with the overall situation come out in their behavior. They would bicker with each other and exhibited attention seeking behaviors like acting out and separation anxiety. They were bored at home all day, but whenever I tried to set up time for them out of the house, they refused to go if I wouldn't be there. This anxiety was a symptom of my anxiety and the overall effect of caring for their baby sister.

I feel a lot of guilt concerning my older girls thinking back to that summer because so much of my attention was focused on our cutie. Each day was such a struggle to keep their baby sister calm and comfortable, that everyone else's needs were lost in the shuffle. Looking back, I don't know if there is anything I could have done different to improve the daily struggle. Maybe I could have gotten a sitter to take the girls to do something while I stayed at home with their sister. Maybe I could have sent them to summer camps. But then they wouldn't have been home with me (which is where they really wanted to be). I think that summer was what it was, and it taught us a lot about what it means to be a family.

If your cutie has any older siblings, it is good to keep in mind that their lives will be impacted throughout the clubfoot treatment as well. You will not be able to change their experience of being a sibling to their clubfoot cutie, but you can be aware of their experience and validate any feelings they have about it. I recommend that when you explain the diagnosis, you do it with clear and concise language, that is age appropriate, while focusing on any positive you can point out. Take the time to answer their questions and validate their concerns but reassure them that everything will turn out okay. As your cutie goes through treatment, try to check in with them about how they are feeling and if there is anything that they need. Bring them into the experience by allowing them to help where they can and tell them how lucky your cutie is to have them in their family. Then give yourself grace when they say that they feel like the baby is getting all the attention, because it might be the truth. And while it might make you feel guilty, remember that you are doing the best you can for everyone in your family.

My older girls learned that all people are born different. Some differences can be seen on the outside and some are internal, but we are all different. Sometimes being a part of a family means putting someone else's needs before your own. Their baby sister needed their mom, and they graciously gave her what she needed, even if they didn't consciously know they were doing it. They learned to be selfless and learned to do things on their own, like get their own snacks from the pantry or go into the backyard to play on their own. Their sister being born with clubfoot impacted their experience in the world and while some of it was a struggle, some of it spurred growth that was so beautiful.

What Do I Say?

With any baby that has something visually "different" about them, there are bound to be looks and questions. When your baby is wearing their BnB you are sure to get some quizzical looks when you are out in public. A week or so after our baby started BnB, I went to the zoo with my best friend and her kids. I felt hyper-aware of everyone looking at us. I saw kids point to the BnB and then turn to their parents in search of an explanation. I saw adults glance at her, look down at her feet, then back up to me, and then quickly look away. It felt weird. I won't say bad, because it didn't feel bad, it was just different. That was it; my baby was different and anyone who saw her knew that she was.

Now, you need to understand how adorable my baby was! I am talking "the works:" big blue eyes, round rosy cheeks, and a mass of curly dark brown hair to boot. She got attention anywhere we went because of how cute she is. As she grew bigger her personality garnered even more attention. She played the "attention seeking game" where she waited until someone made eye contact with her, then flash the most amazing smile, and then immediately turned and hid her face against my shoulder like she was shy and didn't just do the whole thing on purpose. She often caught people's attention because of her charm, but they always continued to look at her because of her BnB. Most of the time I didn't care. But, alas, I'm human and at times it made me feel irritated. Especially when people stared and whispered, but never asked about it. Asking was *always* better. When people asked about her BnB, I got a chance to explain and also spread awareness about clubfoot. Maybe when they asked, I felt better because I got to control the narrative. I can't control what people think, but I could control my response. How I explained her BnB was always under my control. I could focus on positive language that was also informative and straight to the point.

Honestly, in the midst of it, I wasn't consciously making these choices. I just said what felt right. Now looking back at it, I realize how being in control of the explanation helped me feel more in control in general. If I could go back, I would try to be more aware of what I wanted to say when I was asked about her BnB. Your response may be different than mine, or you might just ignore those glances in general. Do what works for you. But be prepared to get looks and questions when you are in public, unless you plan to spend the entire time your baby is 23-hour wear at home!

However, even if you spend most of your time at home, you're bound to have family over, and those family members will have questions too. I felt the most frustrated with these questions. I know our family was asking out of love and good intentions, but for some reason these queries annoyed me the most.

I often felt like I was answering the same questions repeatedly, and that no one in our family was truly listening to my responses. I cannot tell you how many times I was asked, "how long does she have to wear those?" Not just by family, but by friends and acquaintances as well. People who I felt like I'd told a hundred times still asked it every time they saw our cutie in her BnB. I couldn't help but get annoyed! I also think there was an underlying feeling that people saw our cutie's clubfoot and its treatment as her most defining feature, and this irritated me. Here I had the most adorable baby, who was developing typically, hitting all of her milestones at the same time or before her peers, but all anyone wanted to talk about was her BnB and clubfoot treatment. In hindsight, I believe I felt so aggravated because of my own emotional state and processing. I was living my cutie's clubfoot treatment every moment of every day, and it was hard to understand how people couldn't remember the basic course of her treatment. If you've ever had a loved one pass away, you may be familiar with a similar feeling. In mourning, your entire existence is clouded by grief, while those around you who have not suffered the same loss continue on with life as usual. Dealing with those who were "living life as usual" while my world revolved around my cutie's treatment often felt like this.

I was in the trenches of clubfoot treatment, moving through it by what felt like inches at a time while everyone else seemed to be running by. I mean they were lapping me with how fast they were going. Every once in a while, they would stop and be like why are you in the mud? I wanted to scream, "I already told you!!!! Please don't keep asking me!!" Thankfully, I didn't. I politely answered their questions and tried to remain positive while doing so, but that doesn't mean that I didn't want to hurl the BnB against the nearest wall sometimes.

Let's face it, clubfoot treatment is tedious, often frustrating and yes, there will be moments when it seems never-ending. Often you will feel married to the BnB schedule of free time, brace-time, and stretches while everyone else is taking their flexible schedule for granted. There will be times when other people's comments will bother you more than others. You might even snap at someone out of frustration or exhaustion. It's understandable! Give yourself some grace and try to prepare yourself before entering a situation that might be triggering for you.

For example, before a family function I might say to my husband, "It's going to be annoying when everyone asks the same questions about her BnB that I've already answered a hundred times!" He simply says, "Yeah, I know." (He is the best by the way). But just voicing my frustration before entering the situation takes the edge off. Then when someone asked, we steal a glance at each other, give a quick smile, and answer the question again. I also remind myself that their interest is out of love and concern and that they most likely didn't remember the basics of the treatment not because it wasn't important to them but simply because it wasn't a part of their daily life.

When I asked my husband why these questions didn't seem to bother him, he said that he thought of it as an easy conversation point for people. So even if they knew the answer, they would ask the questions again because it was an easy way to start a conversation. I had never looked at it this way because I was looking at it through my own emotional lens. What I found annoying because of my own emotional state didn't bother my husband because he had a different perspective.

The same could be true for you and your partner. Because we were able to communicate our emotions openly with each other without judgment, I could tell him how annoying I thought it was, and he could tell me why it didn't bother him. It is great to check in with yourself regarding the driving factors behind your emotional responses and even better to be able to communicate openly with your partner about them.

Pity

Now, I can sit here and tell you that I was never really truly bothered or upset over stranger's looks or family concerns, but that is not entirely true. Pity! There I said it. That dirty word. The word I hated the most. The one that made me feel like I wanted to crawl out of my skin. Pity, the four-letter word that has the ability to drive me to the brink. When someone made a comment that had the faintest hint of pity in it, it would set my heart afire. Pity is defined as "the feeling of sorrow and compassion caused by the suffering and misfortune of others and a course for regret or disappointment (Webster's Dictionary)." There are three main words in this definition that drove me crazy: misfortune, regret and disappointment. My daughter has not ever been a regret or disappointment to me or my family, clubfoot included. She has never once disappointed me in her journey, and I know she never will. She is strong and resilient, and I'm extremely proud of her every day. I will be damned if she grows up feeling sorry for herself!

Her difference is what makes her unique, it will shape her personality, and I do not regret her being born exactly the way she was meant to be. I don't want people to think it was a misfortune that she was born with a birth defect because she is amazing. She is living proof that our struggles make us stronger. I wouldn't change this about her.

You might be thinking, "You wouldn't want to keep your daughter from experiencing pain and discomfort?" Well, of course I don't want her to feel pain, just like I don't want my older girls to feel pain either, but I can't prevent it. I can support them through it, I can walk with them, hold them, kiss them, cry with them, and console them, but I cannot prevent it. I couldn't prevent my cutie's diagnosis, and I couldn't prevent her from feeling pain, but I can be there for her. I can bounce her on an exercise ball for hours on end to help soothe her and send her to sleep. I can kiss her feet and tickle her thighs until she can't help but giggle. I can do everything in my power to provide her comfort in her boots by buying expensive socks and applying foot glide religiously. I can be her mom. I cannot feel sorry for her being born the way she was meant to be.

So, I say to those with their pitying looks and words, please save your pity for someone who wants it. We clubfoot parents don't need to hear "poor baby," because our cuties are warrior babies. Their clubfoot is not sad, but their strength *is* inspiring. We don't want to hear comments couched in a tone of pity! So, to those who can't help themselves we say, "Can't you see how strong and resilient this baby is! Isn't my cutie amazing?" Turning a negative emotion into a positive one would have helped me reframe these pity-tinged conversations. I had to take their pity and turn it into power. If someone wanted to express pity about my daughter's clubfoot, I didn't have the ability to control it, but I could control my response. I could take what they perceived as a disappointment or a regret and turn it into an embodiment of strength and perseverance. So, if pity drives you mad and is a trigger for you as well, remember that you can choose your response. You are in control of what you say, and you get to tell your cutie's story, and you can choose to tell it anyway you like.

It helped us to focus on as much positivity as we could throughout the casting and BnB phase. Frankly, my husband is 'Mr. Positive.' If you googled what a positive person looks like his picture would probably show up (only kidding). But in all seriousness, he has always led from a place of positivity. Every personality test he has ever taken has placed him in a positive-centric category. So when we face difficulties in life, he usually looks at it from an optimistic standpoint and our daughter's clubfoot was no different. We spent a lot of time focusing on the positive aspects of the diagnosis, like the fact that it was treatable and after successful treatment she would live a typical life.

I reminded myself how the clubfoot diagnosis didn't change anything about all the things I wanted for her as a human. I wanted her to grow up to be confident, kind, assertive, happy, and passionate. Her being born with clubfoot wasn't going to negatively impact any of those things. In fact, it could enhance them in ways we never knew. My husband and I chose to focus on positive ways to explain the treatment to people as well. We would break it down into terms that seemed non-scary and easy to understand. My favorite metaphor to use that seemed to be universally understandable was about braces on your teeth. The casts act like the braces putting the teeth in the correct place, and the BnB was the retainer that keep them in place.

We would explain that similar to your teeth, their feet would move back inwards if they didn't wear the BnB. The casts correct feet, and the BnB keep them that way. We would inevitably get questioned about the length of time wearing the BnB was required. Most people go wide eyed in shock when I answer 4-5 years. I would explain that children go through so many growth spurts during these first four years and wearing the BnB is the best chance to prevent relapse. This analogy also made it seem doable. Once they understood it took away some of the negativity surrounding the treatment and diagnosis.

List of tips for dealing with the inevitable questions:

- Think of responses before you are in public.

- Connect with your own emotional response before reacting.

- Communicate with your partner about your feelings.

- Stay positive.

- Acknowledge trigger words and look for the power behind them.

- Find an easy example or comparison to explain (braces for us).

Support

Let's face it, there aren't many parts of your life that will not be directly impacted by your cutie's clubfoot treatment, so you are going to need support. It is vital that you find a way to get support during your cutie's intense medical care and your subsequent shift to becoming their primary care provider with BnB. I will spend the next chapter (yes it needs its own chapter), discussing how to go about getting the support you will need during this time.

CHAPTER 11

FINDING THE RIGHT SUPPORT

ONE OF THE MAIN REASONS I felt compelled to write this book was to address the issue of support for parents of clubfoot kiddos, particularly those going through the Boots and Bar stage of treatment. When my little one entered the BnB stage, I remember distinctly feeling like I had no support. I had no one to call with questions and very limited resources. I desperately wanted something that I could turn to for guidance and advice with whatever I was struggling with in that minute. Whether it was sleep, blisters, boot fit, heel placement, or schedule, I felt like I had a million questions and no one to ask. I found resources on the internet through a couple of clubfoot websites and there were quite a few social media groups where I could have sought out advice, but nothing that really felt like a good fit for me, support-wise. I didn't feel like I could ask our doctor at the time as he seemed to minimize the questions that we had, and I always felt like I was bothering him. I didn't feel comfortable seeking advice from virtual strangers on the social media groups, and I didn't feel like my family and friends could understand because they were not directly dealing with it. So, I became rather isolated. I wasn't sure how to seek out the support I really needed. So, I just didn't.

Discussed Topics:

- Social media
  - o   Gathering support
  - o   Sharing your story
- Finding a support group
- Family and friends support

- Self-care

- Burn-out

- My therapy journey

- Postpartum anxiety

- It's not fair

- First birthday celebration

- Charity

Social Media

In today's world, there is not a topic out there that isn't impacted by social media and the clubfoot journey and its treatment is no different. Social media outlets like Facebook and Instagram can be a great way to gather support and get more information, but they can also be a black hole that is difficult to escape! I'm going to break our experience with social media into two sections: using social media for support and information gathering, and our decision-making around sharing our cutie's story on social media.

Gathering Support

In this day and age (I felt old writing that, but hey it seems to work so go with me!) whenever we need more information on a topic, the very first thing we do is Google it. From there, we often go on social media to find groups to join or hashtags to follow. This is the primary way of getting information and support in the digital age. But it is important to consider how you want to access and utilize this support.

When our OB diagnosed our daughter with clubfoot, she warned us not to research anything online. And believe me, I really tried. While my husband promptly ignored her warning and immediately began researching clubfoot online, I genuinely tried to avoid the internet. But I was desperate for information! I needed something to help me understand this diagnosis that wouldn't leave me in a panic. In cursory Google searches I found Betsy Miller's book *A Parent's Guide to Clubfoot* and ordered it from Amazon. A lifelong reader, I digest information in literary form better than any other. I also tend to trust the information provided in published works more than information found online. And to be real, when you google "clubfoot" you're immediately confronted with some frightening stuff. Books seemed like the safer option. While waiting for my book (yes, I ordered an actual, physical book), I turned to Facebook to see what other information I could find. I was not on Instagram at this point. I was obviously late to the 'gram game. I looked for clubfoot groups and ended up joining a few closed groups.

- Baby-wearing for Clubfoot

- Clubfoot Connection (Formerly Clubfoot Mommas)

- Clubfoot Moms

- Clubfoot Colorado

Since the groups were closed, I had to send a request to join, which then had to be approved by the administrator of the group. It was difficult for me to request to join these groups because it made everything seem more real. But I wanted to hear from other clubfoot parents (or at least I thought I did). The Clubfoot Colorado page doesn't get a lot of action, but I was able to look through the history for information about doctors trained in Ponseti Method in Colorado. It was through this group that we found our first doctor (who did our cutie's castings in Colorado). I also discovered an important support system through this group, which I will talk more about later.

Baby-wearing for Clubfoot is focused on how to correctly carry your cutie throughout castings and BnB. Occasionally there are posts about things other than baby-wearing, but its primary goal is to educate clubfoot parents on this topic. I used this group as a reference to buy a baby carrier, but my cutie never really liked being in any carrier, so I didn't use it much after that. Numerous moms post photos of their cuties in various baby carriers to get advice about the fit and positioning of the baby when wearing the BnB. The comments are usually helpful, and the group members are supportive on this topic.

Clubfoot Connection has many members and is active with several posts a day. I joined the group shortly after I found out about my daughter's clubfoot and immediately found it overwhelming. There were so many posts every day that it showed up on my newsfeed constantly. Also, it seemed like most of the posts were about issues parents were facing with their cutie. The group was adding to my anxiety every time I looked on Facebook. I ended up having to turn off all notifications from the group. That way, the only way I could see any new posts or comments was if I went into the group itself.

You have to understand that in the few weeks initially following her diagnosis, I felt like all I could think about was her clubfeet. I even remember asking my husband if there would come a time when I wouldn't think about it every five minutes. Because of my anxiety, I tend to obsess and ruminate on things. After the diagnosis, I was already thinking about clubfoot non-stop, so I didn't need any extra pushes in that direction. If you are anything like me, the onslaught of information can feel overwhelming. Add in the pregnancy hormones and it can absolutely feel like too much.

I felt overwhelmed, but I also felt torn. I didn't want to leave the group entirely because I needed information, and I wanted to hear directly from other parents going through the treatment. While I was learning a lot, I was going to have to manage my interaction with the group in a way that worked for me. So, I allowed myself to look at the group feed once a day and only when I was alone or just with my husband. That way, if I became emotional or overwhelmed, I wouldn't transfer it into my parenting. These boundaries worked for me for a couple of months, and when I felt I had learned enough, I decided to leave the group altogether.

While Clubfoot Connection added to my anxiety at times, it also served an invaluable purpose for me. It made me aware of all the potential issues we could face. I read the posts about slipped casts, rocker bottom, blisters, pressure sores, relapse after relapse, forgetting your cutie's BnB when going out of town, stretches, very difficult transitions to BnB, and doctors who said they were doing Ponseti but weren't. It all scared me straight. I saw all the potential issues we could face, and I became aware that clubfoot and its treatment was not always simple and straightforward. In fact, it can be quite complicated.

It is in this group that I first heard about Dr. Dobbs and all the amazing work he does. It is where I learned about the best doctors in Colorado for treatment. It is where I learned to trust my gut and my mom intuition, because if I felt like something was wrong, then it probably was. I gained a lot of valuable information from being in this group and there were some positive posts such as, "Let's hear stories of nice things people said to you when your baby was wearing their BnB." There were many wonderful stories from that post that I still remember to this day. And I loved watching the videos of other cuties who had reached various milestones like crawling, cruising, walking, running and jumping. Those videos bolstered me, but because they were less frequent than people requesting advice on certain issues, I would internalize all the potential problems as ones we would face with our daughter. I couldn't stop myself from playing worst-case scenarios, and there came a point where I had to pull myself off the moving train and remind myself that people who posted were looking for help for their situation and that did not mean it would be mine.

Maybe you are completely different than me, and you don't struggle with anxiety and worrying. You may find comfort in the group and even end up leading your own group one day. I encourage you to find what works for you and to do what feels best. That might mean setting some limits; it might mean being an active participant.

Sharing Your Story on Social Media

Another decision we had to make regarding social media was how much of our cutie's journey we were going to share with the online community. You will inevitably have to make a similar decision with your own cutie. Your journey may look different from ours, but I recommend that you make conscious decisions about what you choose to post about your cutie. This doesn't mean that you shouldn't post about your child and their walk through clubfoot treatment. It simply means to be aware of what you choose to post. As we're all aware, once you post anything on the internet, there's no way of getting it back. I follow the #clubfootcutie on Instagram, and I've enjoyed viewing the stories and pictures of other cuties out there. These images and stories have brought me some joy in moments of anxiety about my cutie's treatment. I love seeing all the cuties in their casts (some decorated like you wouldn't believe) and their BnB, with their adorable bar covers!

My husband and I are on social media, and we have shared pictures of our older girls and our family. However, we are not frequent posters. Even before we had our cutie, we were very conscious about the pictures that we posted of our girls on the internet. I didn't want any photos of my girls that they would not be comfortable with when they were older made available to the world without their consent. We never post photos of any type of nudity simply because of privacy and safety concerns.

When it came time to decide whether we would share our daughter's clubfoot diagnosis and any subsequent treatment, we decided that we wanted to keep her journey off all social media. I do post pictures of our cutie, and there have been several when she had her casts and leg warmers on, but we never outright shared that she was born with clubfoot or the details of her treatment. We made this choice for a few reasons. First, I didn't want the focus of her first few years of life to be about her birth defect and its treatment. Secondly, I didn't think it was entirely my story to share. As I stated before, this book is my story of caring for my cutie, but it is not her story of growing up with clubfoot. I don't want to speak for her, and I couldn't figure out a way around that if I chose to share her journey on social media.

I am thankful for the families who have chosen to share the ins and outs of their cutie's treatment and progress, because it provides valuable information for other clubfoot parents. The stories these families choose to share help to create a clubfoot community and make parents helping their cuties through treatment feel less isolated. It was not the decision that I made for my cutie, but it is by no means the wrong decision. All of our journeys through clubfoot treatment are going to be slightly different, all I suggest you do is to think before you post. Think about what you want to share and what your cutie will see as they grow. And remember, once your stories and images make their way into the spiderweb of the internet, there is no real way of getting them back.

Finding a Support Group

Thankfully, while I was pregnant with my cutie, I had the opportunity to meet a few fellow pregnant moms who knew their babies would be born with clubfoot. All of the babies would be less than two months apart in age. We all ended up doing treatment within in the same hospital, and four of us all saw the same doctor for the casting phase. Our babies were separated by a few weeks in age, so they were inevitably in different phases of treatment but most of us were in casting around the same time.

We were all strangers before we made the effort to meet up and share our stories and experiences, but these other moms became my lifeline. They filled the void in my support group. We ended up creating a private Facebook group where we could share our experiences and seek advice throughout the casting phase and transition to BnB. I can't tell you enough how much theses other moms meant (and still mean) to me. It was these moms that I turned to late at night when I had questions about heel placement or whether or not I should crisscross the straps of my cutie's boots. I spent hours messaging them with questions, thoughts, and bouncing ideas back and forth. I trusted their opinions and felt comfortable asking what I thought were dumb questions because I knew they wouldn't judge me and probably had the same questions too. I knew that when they asked me questions, I never thought they were dumb, which probably meant they felt the same way about mine.

When I started to question whether or not my daughter's feet were fully corrected, it was them that I turned to first. It was them who guided me to our new doctor and who also reassured me that her feet looked great, but a second opinion never hurts. I feel so lucky that I met these women when I did, and that I felt like I had someone to walk through this journey with. It wasn't just that we were going through similar experiences, but also that we approached it in such a similar manner. We are all hyper-vigilant, ask a lot of questions, and tend to worry more than we should. I honestly don't know what I would have done without them and I know they felt the same way because we all expressed it frequently.

One of my dreams is to help other clubfoot parents find a buddy system so they can have the same experience that I did in my group. Having someone to turn to, who has either experienced it or is currently experiencing it, can be the best possible source of support. It was vital for me to have people I could talk to who I knew would tell me the truth, were getting similar medical information, and had the same attitude towards treatment as I did. This extra support is especially necessary when your cutie transitions to BnB, because this is when the bulk of the treatment is placed on your shoulders. You will need as much support as you can get.

The support of a fellow parent can help you feel less isolated and give you that extra boost of support when you need it most. There were several times that I messaged the group about minor concerns just to get their feedback or simply have them commiserate. This was all done virtually; while we have met a couple of times in person, the bulk of our communication was formed via messaging and the internet. I am not anti-social media, although I am simply wary of sharing too much information on a platform that I cannot control. I think that they can be powerful tools to connect people when utilized to best fit your needs, but I didn't feel comfortable seeking support from large groups. The private closed group we created on Facebook did wonders for me by providing much needed support when I wasn't able to find it elsewhere. Maybe the large groups are more your jam and they provide the support you need more than anything else. You may have to adjust to find the social support that works best for your needs.

Whatever the support is that you need, you need to find and connect with other people who are going through similar experiences. Making these connections with other parents can combat the feelings of isolation that can form when your child is going through treatment. Be brave and put yourself out there:

- Join a group or ask your doctor if they know of any support groups they can connect you with.

- Direct message someone on social media in your area and see if they are interested in getting together.

- Email a clubfoot website and ask if they have any references for support groups. To get the support that you need, you may have to venture out of your comfort zone.

That is how I found my friend group. I saw a post on a clubfoot Facebook group that said they were planning a dinner, and I asked if I could join. I live the furthest away which meant a two-hour drive, but I wanted to put myself out there. While I drove to that dinner, I felt incredibly nervous, because I was meeting complete strangers and making myself vulnerable. I was pregnant with my cutie, and I had not processed all the emotions about the diagnosis, and now I was going to have to talk with strangers about it. I was so happy I stepped out of my comfort zone, because if I hadn't, I would never have met the women who came to serve as my main support through treatment.

I encourage you to do the same, even if it feel uncomfortable. Push yourself to open up to opportunities that may lend much needed support in the future. Reach out to people, and if you don't make a connection with the first person, keep trying until you do. Take the steps to create your own clubfoot community to provide the support you need in the moments you need it. I hope that in the future there will be more readily available support groups for parents of clubfoot kids going through various stages of treatment, but until that time comes, you will have to create the support that you need.

We all need each other for support and sometimes we need a push from other moms in a positive and helpful way. When you are good at something, like advocating for your child, don't be afraid to talk about it with other moms. Focus on encouraging them in a positive and uplifting way that will leave them wanting to do the same. You have to think about how you are approaching it before you do it. If you have a strength, a talent or even a common experience with another mom that you want to share, I urge you to do it! But always consider using a helpful and supportive approach.

A great example of this approach is illustrated by a fellow clubfoot mom, whose cutie is about a month older than my daughter. We both took our cuties to the same local doctor. This mom ran into a bump in treatment during the casting phase and made the decision to seek treatment elsewhere. She could have used the opportunity to completely malign our doctor for his mistreatment of her cutie's foot, but she didn't. She explained her reasoning behind switching but said that she still thought that our current doctor was a great doctor, just not the right doctor for her baby's foot. Even when I pressed her on the specifics about what she thought our current doctor did wrong, she didn't go into a diatribe about all the things he could have done differently. She simply stated that she thought her cutie's foot was more complicated than he had anticipated. When we later made the decision to get a second opinion from her new doctor (Dr. Dobbs) about our cutie's treatment, she was completely supportive and extremely informative without having a "know it all" or "I told you so" attitude. Looking back at it now, I am so grateful for how my friend was able to share her experience and subsequent knowledge in a way that wasn't fear-inducing or shaming. This experience made me feel comfortable to trust her with any issues I might face with my cutie in the future.

Family and Friends Support

I probably have one of the most supportive families in the world. I'm not just saying that. I really mean it. My mom and I are extremely close. How close, you ask? She was my matron of honor at my wedding, that's how close. My dad and I have similar personalities and have grown closer as I have gotten older. I have 3 brothers who all live in nearby and I know

I can turn to them when I need help. While we are like any family, with family dynamics that impact our relationships, at the end of the day we genuinely love and support one another.

Yet, when I found out about my daughter's clubfoot diagnosis, I didn't tell them all right away. I called my mom who was waiting to hear how the ultrasound went, but I didn't want to tell anyone else. I felt paralyzed in the moment and felt like maybe if I didn't tell anyone, the diagnosis wouldn't be real. I'm not entirely sure what the motivation was behind my response. All I know is that I didn't want to reach out for the support that I knew would be there.

I eventually told my whole family, and my husband's family about the diagnosis, but I held on to that feeling of protectiveness about the diagnosis throughout my pregnancy and her first few months of treatment. I knew that people wanted to help, and they consistently offered their support, but I didn't know how to receive it from them.

I was open to sharing my experience with the other moms in my clubfoot group, but I didn't know how to explain or connect with people who didn't have direct experience with what I was going through. I knew they could listen and provide empathy as they had in many other situations before, but somehow this felt different. I felt more closed off than I had before, and I didn't know how to share my experience adequately. Looking back, I wish I had shared more and reached out for support from my immediate family, because I think it would have helped me feel less isolated during those extremely tough 23-hour BnB wear months.

It was during the BnB transition that I really struggled to connect with the people around me. I was home with all three of my daughters five days a week (thank you, summer break) and could barely keep my head above water. My cutie was not sleeping at night for more than 1-2 hours at a time and seemed miserable throughout the day. It took everything I had to simply stay afloat. Yet, I rarely reached out for support. Sure, I called my mom several times a day, but rarely did I ask her to come over and help. Yes, I chatted with my brothers, but I never really stopped to explain how hard it was or took them up on their offers to help. I never truly let people into my world.

One day, about 3 weeks into 23-hour BnB, my stepmother-in-law came over for a visit. My cutie was in a constant state of unhappy that day.

I tried absolutely everything to calm her, yet nothing seemed to work. A couple of weeks after that visit, we were having dinner together when she mentioned that she didn't know how I managed to do that all day every day. I think she even referred to me as a saint, which was probably the first and last time that has happened.

However, she was witness to the amount of work it took to keep my cutie calm and relaxed while parenting my other young children. I remember thinking that I should feel embarrassed or ashamed that she saw me struggle, but instead I felt a sense of relief. Finally, someone had witnessed the messy reality of "a day in the life of a clubfoot parent."

I wish I would have had the courage to be more vulnerable and let my family and immediate friends see my struggle. Maybe I would have felt less alone. Maybe I would have felt more understood and maybe that would have pushed me to accept help more often. I honestly don't know whether or not it would have changed my experience, but I wish I would have let more people in.

If you are a family member or a close friend to a parent whose child is in the first 6 months of clubfoot treatment these are a few recommendations for you to support this person as best as you can.

- Simply show up - Be there and witness their experience.

- Praise their efforts - Vocalize what you have witnessed and praise them for all the work they have done.

- Offer to help - Bring coffee, a meal, donuts, cookies, health bars - whatever you can do to let them know that you see them.

- Get Specific - If they refuse help, be more specific in what help you are offering. Tell them I am going to bring you a coffee, what kind would you like? Or I am sending a cleaning person over next week, what day works best?

- Actively listen - Lend a listening ear and allow the parent to vent or complain when needed.

- Ask how they are doing - Then listen and respond with love and empathy.

- Don't be afraid to have the hard conversation- If you see your loved struggling and are concerned for their safety and mental health, sit down and talk with them about what you are experiencing.

I want to take a moment to touch on the last bullet point because I think it is really important. If you are witnessing your friend of family member struggle outside what you think is healthy, don't be afraid to have a hard conversation with them. All new parents are in the throes of the newborn stage and they may not even know how much they are struggling until you point it out to them. This is especially true for parents who are dealing with medical issues and special needs because we are hyper-focused on the care of our babies that we often don't have the wherewithal to see how much we are struggling. The conversation may be difficult and it might be uncomfortable for both of you, but you do not want to regret not offering help when you can. You don't have to have answers to their problems; simply witnessing their experience and offering to help them in whatever way possible can be life changing for people. So don't be afraid, don't wait, have courage, be vulnerable and take the moment to share your love and support with that person by telling them that you see them and you are here for them.

Look, it's hard to help someone going through a difficult and rigorous experience with their child, especially if they are like me and are averse to help. However, it was helpful to just have people there to listen and commiserate with. So just show up in-person, by phone, or via email. Send notes saying that they are on your mind and you are sending positive thoughts or prayers.

To build your own support network, draw from the following resources:

- Immediate family
- Extended family
- Friends
- Clubfoot Friends
- Medical Provider
    o   Medical provider team (nurses)
    o   Physical Therapy
- Social media groups

- Therapist
- Clubfoot websites
- Pediatrician

Self-Care

I am certainly not an expert in self-care, and during my daughter's most intense months of treatment (casting and transition to BnB) I did a poor job of taking care of myself. I struggled with major bouts of anxiety and was not utilizing my resources to help care for myself. Let's face it, 23-hour wear can be brutal. You are caring for your child 24 hours a day, and if your baby is anything like mine, there are days when you will do everything you can think of to try and make them happy to no avail. This intense level of caregiving left little time for me to care for myself, or even have the mental capacity to think about, caring for myself. I didn't have the brain space to think about what I needed to provide care for myself, let alone try to go out and make it happen.

I was getting little to no sleep at night. I was trying to parent two older, active girls, and I was attempting to keep up with managing our house (i.e. laundry, cleaning, cooking). I wasn't exercising, making healthy food choices, reading enough, taking breaks, seeing a therapist, or going to acupuncture. I never got my hair cut or my nails done. I wasn't doing anything to focus on caring for myself.

I am a believer of the old adage that in order to care for your loved ones, you must first care for yourself. But to be clear, I am a *believer* and not a *follower*. I wish I had done it differently. I wish I could go back and talk to that mom and gently remind her that it was okay to think about herself for a moment and to ask for what she needs to move forward. Here are some things that would have helped me (and might help you too):

- Exercise - Walk, do a 10-minute online workout, take the stroller around the block a few times, just get moving somehow.

- Take a bath - Let your partner handle the load for 20 minutes and take a bath (or a shower) and just release and relax.

- Read a book - Read a new book (or an old favorite) while baby is napping and let your mind go somewhere else.

- Eat one vegetable a day - Something as simple as carrots with hummus, so you are nourishing your body with one thing you can be proud of.

- Take a break - Have lunch or coffee with a friend, leave the baby with your partner.

- Order in your favorite food for dinner - Treat yourself to something that you love. You deserve it.

- Play with your older kids (if you have them) - Slow down, leave the dishes, and do something focused on your other kids.

- Pay someone to clean your house - Maybe only once, maybe even if it is just the bathrooms, but take something off your plate.

- Sleep extra when you can - On the weekend sleep in while your partner gets up or try to nap when the baby is sleeping (even just once a week).

- Use your mantra - Find a mantra to repeat to yourself in moments of stress.

- Utilize outside resources - Acupuncture, yoga, meditation, therapy, chiropractor, massage, whatever works for you, find it and try it.

You will inevitably need different types of support during different stages of treatment and what that support looks like might change. I needed the most support during the transition to BnB and the 3 months of 23-hour wear. I remember counting down the weeks, saying to myself "only 11 more to go, I can make it." Once our cutie went down to 18-hour wear, things opened up a bit more, but trying to accommodate the BnB wear schedule was still trying. Also, the support looked different at this stage because I needed more help with the timing of it all, mixed with my other girls' schedules of school and extracurricular activities. Once she was in 12-hour wear and walking around like a champ, support looked more like congratulating us on her progress and asking about how things were going. At this stage, most people would never know unless I told them about her clubfoot, so I stopped getting as many outside inquiries about her treatment.

Another thing that helped me was to start using a mantra when I was feeling overwhelmed and stressed. I told myself to "be brave." In moments of weakness and self-doubt, I reminded myself to "be brave." It only took a moment, and it would remind me that I was strong.

This mantra helped me to remember how brave my cutie had been throughout this process. She showed me strength and resilience every day, and she taught me about true bravery. I encourage you to take this opportunity to think of a mantra of your own. It should be a word or phrase that reminds you of your inner strength and centers your thoughts while in this phase of treatment.

Perhaps your mantra is something that has helped you in the past, or maybe you need to find something entirely new. You may even have to try out a few mantras before you find what fits. Personally, I used "be brave" so often that I started to say it to my older daughters, and it inevitably became a family mantra. I even had it tattooed on my ankle as a reminder of how far my cutie and I have come together, and what it has meant for our entire family.

Here are a few mantras you might try out:

- Breathe

- One step at a time

- I am strong and capable

- Just keep going

- I've got this

- Never give up

- It always seems impossible until it's done. - Nelson Mandela

Burn Out

I was talking with a fellow clubfoot mom, on one of the travel days for clubfoot checkups, and we started talking about burnout. Her son had just turned one and she said that she had hit a point where she was tired of doing the stretches numerous times a day and putting on the boots and trying to manage the sleepless nights. She was burnt out. She was tired of doing it all. But of course, she wouldn't stop treatment in any fashion. She is an amazingly strong mom who has been a warrior and advocate for her son throughout his treatment. So, if she could get burnt out, what hope do the rest of us have? If she wanted to give up, how would the rest of us carry on?

I was so grateful that she vocalized how she was feeling because it normalized these feelings. Her saying she was tired of it all allowed me to let my guard down a little and tap into similar feelings I was experiencing. Sometimes when someone is able to put words to emotions that you may be feeling but not acknowledging, it can provide space for you to accept those feelings as your own. This clubfoot treatment journey is long and can be grueling, and I think it is inevitable that we all feel burn out at some point during the 4-5 years our child is in treatment.

It is important to acknowledge these moments and even talk about them with a partner, a close friend, or a fellow clubfoot parent. It doesn't mean that you will stop treatment or stretches and give up, it means that you are accepting your own feelings and how they impact your child's journey. Just saying "this is hard" and "I'm tired" to a fellow human can be enough to allow you to be seen. Once you are seen, you can keep moving forward. I think there are other things you can do to re-energize yourself through a burn out phase and here are a few things that worked for me:

- Talk about your feelings with someone you trust

- Write about your experience - Obviously this has helped me.

- Reread a book or article that helped you cope with the initial diagnosis to help you remember why this treatment is so important.

- Schedule a get-together with people who understand.

- Work on a project that reminds you why you are doing this, even something as simple as a footprint of your cutie!

- Let your partner help when they can - My husband took charge of bedtime so that I had a break from it all, since I was in charge all day.

- Reach out - Take time for anything that allows you to re-energize, like exercise, therapy, massage, nails, coffee and bookstore break, something that is self-care.

The truth is, most parents will experience burn out at some point during clubfoot treatment and when you do, you can acknowledge it, work through it and keep on moving. I know it is exhausting and can feel never ending, but it is worth it in the end. You are doing it all so that your child can live a healthy, active, and pain-free life.

My Therapy Journey

About five months after my cutie was born, I realized that I was struggling with some pretty significant anxiety. I have always had an anxious brain, and the postpartum stress coupled with the intensity of the clubfoot treatment threw me into a familiar anxiety tailspin. I spent countless hours worrying about my cutie's feet and their treatment, even after they were corrected. I worried about my older daughters when they were born too, but this was much more intense. It felt like there was so much pressure to do everything right because the stakes were so high. If we didn't follow the BnB regimen exactly, we risked relapse and having to do further treatment and possibly a more intense and invasive surgery.

My anxiety about her clubfoot started to impact the rest of my life. When we switched doctors and Dr. Dobbs confirmed that her feet were corrected, I thought the anxiety would fall away, but it didn't. It helped me not to worry about her feet as much, but it was then that I realized my anxiety had been the driving force propelling me through the first five months of her life. It was what fueled me to keep pushing forward and provided the adrenaline I needed to get through the tough moments of her BnB transition.

After I heard that her feet were corrected from a doctor I trusted completely, I felt a rush of relief, but my old friend anxiety was still there, and it now needed a new home in which to live. It was a couple of weeks after we received the "all clear" on her feet that I turned to my husband and said, "I think I might have postpartum anxiety."

I had done some research on the topic and saw that much of what I was experiencing emotionally and physically matched the symptoms listed. I read my husband one of the articles aloud and saw his face light up with recognition, because he too could see that the symptoms were very similar to mine. He decided to do some research on his own, and we came to the conclusion together that I needed to see someone about what I was experiencing. It was time for me to find a therapist.

I received my Masters in Marriage and Family therapy in 2012. So, considering my background, it should not surprise you when I say that I deeply believe in therapy. I have gone to therapy several different times in my life, and it has been immensely beneficial. But, after our cutie was born, I wasn't in therapy and needed to find a new therapist. Even for someone who has experienced numerous therapists, it is intimidating to try to find someone new to talk to. I remembered the advice I gave to other people: "it is all about your relationship with your therapist." You have to feel comfortable and trust your therapist, and sometimes it can take talking to a few different therapists before you find the right fit.

Many therapists offer free phone or in person consultations, where you can gauge your comfort level with this person. For me, it is better to do this in-person, but sometimes you can get enough information over the phone to make a decision. If you feel comfortable, try asking family and/or friends if they have any recommendations. Sometimes it is easier if you know someone has had a good experience with someone before trying them out. Take advantage of this option and don't be discouraged and stop looking if the first person you talk to isn't the right fit. There is someone out there who can help you.

While I was pregnant with my daughter, my dad was diagnosed with prostate cancer. So, I spent the last portion of my pregnancy in a highly anxious state. I made an appointment with a therapist who took my insurance because I was worried about all of the medical bills that we were anticipating with labor and delivery and her clubfoot treatment. I met with this therapist once and while it didn't go horribly, it didn't help alleviate my stress or anxiety. I knew immediately that it wasn't the right fit for me. She kept mentioning that I just needed a plan to help relieve my anxiety, and I felt like that was the exact opposite of what I needed. I knew logically that I could plan for the casting and BnB to a certain extent, but my anxiety centered around the unknown.

My mind was swirling with the unknowns: How would I change a diaper with casts? How would my baby sleep at night with a BnB? How would I prevent her from taking them off as she got older? Questions that

I didn't have the answers to, and I couldn't emotionally plan for. What I really needed was someone to help me stay grounded in the present and not spend excessive time worrying about the unknown future.

After we heard about her clubfoot diagnosis, I started to worry about a range of all sorts of issues that *could* be problems we didn't know about yet. I had terrible nightmares and felt so anxious that I had difficulty calming my nerves. My heart would race. It felt like everything around me had stopped and all I could feel was my racing heart. Everything I worried about was completely out of my control. If there was something else wrong with my daughter, there wasn't anything I could do. And if my dad's cancer diagnosis continued to get worse, there was nothing I could do to change it. No amount of planning could change the future. I needed a therapist who could help me work through my present anxiety without continued worry about the future things out of my control.

I was tempted to continue seeing the first therapist I met with, because I knew it wouldn't cost anything and it was easier than starting my search for a new therapist all over again. I even went as far as booking another therapy session with her, but my daughter was born before it occurred, and I had to cancel. Here I was, a trained therapist, and a seasoned therapy goer at that, about to discount my own important advice about finding the right fit. About 5 months after my daughter was born, I found a new therapist recommended by a family member. He is not covered by my insurance, but he helped me develop the skills I needed to combat my anxiety. For me that meant grounding myself in the moment and developing skills to allow myself to sit with difficult emotions instead of immediately trying to fix them. By ignoring or immediately moving past my emotions, I was missing the opportunity to explore why I was feeling that way and address the underlying issues. Once I slowed down and took notice of my emotions, I realized that I had a cycle of negative thoughts.

For example, I found myself saying over and over, "I can't do this" whenever I was feeling overwhelmed or frustrated, I was exhausted, exasperated, and my self-confidence was low. I was able to combat that negative thought with a realistic one. While I might feel like I can't do it, the *reality is* that I am doing it. Now, I didn't do a complete 180 from saying "I can't do this" to "I am killing this right now!" The act of slowing down and grounding myself in the present moment worked for me, but therapy is not a one-size-fits-all program.

Postpartum Anxiety

As someone who has an ongoing struggle with anxiety, it was difficult to differentiate between what was situational anxiety and what was potentially postpartum anxiety. There is a lot of information and awareness surrounding postpartum depression, but postpartum anxiety can be harder to find information on, which may lead people who are struggling to continue to struggle without reaching out for help. In my experience, I knew it was something more intense when I couldn't shake the feeling of anxiety no matter what I tried. I developed physical symptoms, such as racing heartbeat, insomnia, racing thoughts, and physical shaking when nervous. Those physical symptoms in combination with my ruminating negative thoughts, low self-esteem, worst-case scenario thinking, and visions of terrible things happening to my loved ones, lead me to the conclusion that this was something more than what I had struggled with before.

If you find yourself struggling with any of these similar issues, it is important that you check in with yourself and your loved ones to determine if you need to seek further help. While PPA is something that is not as readily diagnosed as PPD, it is something that the medical community is aware of and has experience with, and they can help. The first step is to recognize your symptoms, which can be difficult when you are a mom to a newborn and experiencing so many of the regular "new mom" stuff like exhaustion, fatigue, low energy, trouble sleeping, and feelings of social isolation and loneliness.

For me, it helped to check in with my closest loved ones, which meant my husband and my mom, to see if they had noticed a change in my behavior as well. When you are feeling all of these intense emotions coupled with a big life change, it can leave you feeling confused about what feelings are normal and those which may need more help to address. So, check in with a trusted person in your life and be open to their feedback, and if they verify your feelings, then take the next step to seek help. You can contact your OB, your primary care physician, or a therapist to check in about what you are experiencing, and they will help you figure out what the next steps are. Just know that you are not alone in your experience, so many other moms are struggling and there is absolutely no shame in reaching out for help.

Clubfoot parents, or any parents dealing with their babies' immediate medical or special needs, can be at a greater risk of experiencing mental health issues postpartum due to the intensified experience after birth. While having to care for a newborn, you also have to deal with all the of medical needs as well. When I was researching information about the prevalence of PPA in moms parenting special needs kids I came across a line that really resonated with me. It said, "Parents of children with special needs tend to be faced with a continuous barrage of challenges from societal isolation, financial strain, difficulty finding resources to outright exhaustion or feelings of confusion or burnout (https://www.special-learning.com/article/depression)." While clubfoot is not considered a special need, it is definitely a medical special need until your cutie is out of treatment. As parents of babies that need extensive medical care, I can't help but think that we are more prone to experiencing mental health issues due to the nature of our circumstances.

Here are some symptoms of postpartum anxiety (PPA) symptoms that I read about and could relate to. If you are experiencing these symptoms you may need to seek support.

Postpartum Anxiety Symptoms: from anxietycanda.com

- Increased heart rate
- Loss of appetite
- Difficulty falling or staying asleep
- Racing thoughts about future
- Worst-case scenario thinking
- Worrying and obsessing
- Avoiding
- Over-controlling
- Asking for reassurance constantly

It's Not Fair

When I think back to the moments, hours, and days following my daughter's clubfoot diagnosis, one of my strongest emotional responses was "It's not fair." Like my 4-year old, I wanted to scream it to the universe, and I am sure I uttered it to my husband on several different occasions either out of sadness or anger. The day I found out about her clubfoot diagnosis I vividly remember sitting on my bed completely still, wearing my heavy winter coat that was straining to fit over my protruding belly, staring at the wall, thinking about my unborn child and I endlessly ruminated over this phrase: *it's not fair*. All I could think about were the other 999 babies who were born without clubfoot. Why did my daughter have to be the one? All my neighbors and friends got to have perfectly healthy babies with no health conditions, and they weren't even grateful. It wasn't fair that they got to have healthy babies. Why did they deserve it? What had I done wrong? Why did my child have to overcome such adversity in her first few years of life? I needed someone to blame, someone to be mad at, and it certainly wasn't going to be the tiny human growing inside my body. It was easy to take my anger and guilt out on unknowing and unsuspecting people in my life.

I realize that it may seem like a childish response, as evidenced by the frequency with which my middle child utters the phrase, to proclaim that something was "unfair." I am a grown woman, I have lived, and I certainly know that life isn't fair. I am also certain that I have used the phrase "life isn't fair sometimes" when parenting my older girls. It didn't matter whether it was a childish response or that I should have known better, because it was my emotional response to the situation.

The hours directly after I heard about her diagnosis were spent in confusion, guilt, shame, self-doubt and self-pity, and it would take a while before I was able to make my way up out of that darkness. I think that no matter if you were born with clubfoot, or have a child who has been, or a child born with another unexpected diagnosis, or have lost a job, or lost a relative or friend or beloved pet, the feeling of "unfair" is a relatable one. We have all experienced it in some shape or form and will no doubt experience it several more times throughout our lives. However, this "unfair" feeling in the wake of my cutie's diagnosis was the strongest of its kind that I had ever encountered.

I fell deep into the hole, into the darkness of unfair, and struggled to see the light. What if I never came out? What if I always felt like it was unfair? What if I couldn't find the "reframe?" I think the reality is that there are some things in life that are not fair and trying to find the "fair" in a situation may be emotional, but not entirely rational or logical. If you are searching to find the "fair" aspect of the situation — what is fair about hav-ing a child born with clubfoot? — you may never find the answer.

To this day I don't think it was "fair" that my cutie was born with club-foot, but somewhere in the course of our journey, I was able to see that it was okay. Maybe acceptance was the key. Once I stopped looking for the fair or unfair, the right or wrong, and just accepted what is, I was able to move from the darkness to the light. My daughter was born with clubfoot and it's okay.

First Birthday

I thought I would take a moment to talk about how important the mile-stone of our cutie's first birthday was for us. With my older girls, their first birthdays were always bittersweet because it meant they were no longer infants and were growing up so quickly. With our cutie we had the same feelings, with the extra knowledge of how much she had been through in her first year of life. The first year of life for clubfoot kids usually involves the most intense and strenuous part of their treatment. They have been through several casts, most likely a tenotomy, and wearing their BnB for countless hours. Maybe there were blisters and ingrown toenails. If we are lucky, our cutie's first birthday marks the end of the most difficult part of treatment and we can look forward to continued night-and-nap wear.

While I reflected back on her first year of life, I wanted to create some-thing special for her journey. Something that she could keep and remem-ber (or to show her since she is too young to actually have any memory of it), how far she has come. We kept every cast from her appointments, and I had seen other clubfoot parents use the casts for a display, but frank-ly I couldn't figure out how to get them back together from where they were sawed off. Some of the casts were in better shape than others, but I couldn't figure out how to make them look intact. My grand idea was to display them in a shadow box, and maybe at some point in the future this dream can become a reality, but I wasn't going to be able to make it hap-pen before her first birthday. I will definitely hold on to the casts, whether we display them or not, so that she can have them and see them as she grows.

I decided that if I couldn't get the casts together, then maybe I could do something with the photos I had taken during the casting appoint-ment. I selected several photos from each appointment and put them in a separate album on my phone and then had them all printed. I had an old frame that held 7 photos and decided to pick one photo from each appointment to represent that cast. I tried to make them different to add variety. One image showed the doctor applying the cast, one was a clo-seup of her toes in the cast, and a couple shots pictured her feet showing the progress each cast made. I then wrote the date and number of each cast on the back of the picture so she could look at them and know exact timing. I was so thankful for the iPhone and the date time stamp on each photo so that I didn't have to guess which cast appointment was which. I don't know if I would have remembered them all as they started to blur together the farther we got away from the casts.

When I finished the project, I sent a picture of it to my husband and my mom and they both replied that it made them cry. My husband said it reminded him of how much she had been through during the first year of her life. Their emotional reaction was interesting to me, because while I was working on the project, I didn't feel overly emotional, but once I heard their responses, it made me tap into my emotions as well.

I feel so much pride in my cutie's growth. I look at how joyful she is, and I can't believe that she has made it through so much and she is still just a little baby. I wonder how much of this experience has shaped and will continue to shape her personality. Looking at those pictures made those thoughts all the more real. In the end, I think I like the pictures bet-ter than the casts themselves because, as my mom pointed out, the pic-tures show *her*. You get to see her in the casts and directly living the ex-perience. The focus became more about her and less about the casts she had to wear. I still love the idea of using her casts as original art, and love what I have seen other parents do on social media for their cuties, but for now I am happy with what she has to represent that time in her life. The picture project was a better representation of what she had been through as a human and it showed her personal growth, plus you got to see her adorable face.

I also wrote a children's book based on her clubfoot experience called 'Twinkle Toes' earlier in the year. I wanted to do something with that for her birthday, too. However, I may be able to rhyme some words together, I absolutely cannot draw. Therefore, I needed someone to illustrate my book and I knew that was not going to be an easy task. I asked a couple of my artist friends, but the job was too big and detailed to make it happen in a short timeframe. So, I started to think about different ways I could still utilize it, like printing it as a poem and framing it. Then I came up with the idea of creating a photo book with pictures of her that were good representations of the text. Sure, it wouldn't look exactly the way I had originally envisioned it, but the pictures of her would make it even more personal. But I can tell you it took a lot of time to pick out the right photos to match the text on each page. It was time-consuming and tedious trying to find the photos and then placing them in the right sections of the book, but I ended up really loving the finished product. I was so happy that I was able to do something with the story I had written just for her and put it into a format that I can now read to her consistently. The added bonus is that it has so many pictures of her and her family in it that it is a great tool for her growing recognition as well. I still fully intend to have the story illustrated and hopefully published, because I think it can be universal for all clubfoot kiddos, but for the moment the photo book worked perfectly.

I encourage you to come up with an idea of your own to help you and your cuties commemorate their first birthday because their first year of life will mostly likely be the most difficult treatment-wise. It does not have to be anything elaborate, just something that signifies how much growth you and your child have made in the last year together.

Some ideas that might work for you:

- Write/Illustrate a book
- Do casting photos
- Print out any song lyrics that were meaningful to you both
- Make a quilt with the bar covers
- Frame the boots in a shadow box
- Do a calendar with favorite BnB/Casting photos
- Line up all the casts for a photo
- Ask family members and friends to write down their thoughts on your cutie's journey
- Check social media sites for other clubfoot parents' creative ideas
- Do something completely your own!

Whatever you decide, I encourage you to start the project and see how it progresses. If you need to change course, remember it is something that is for you, your child, and your family to commemorate all the hard work you all put in during this first year of clubfoot treatment.

Charity

We made the decision to ask family and friends to make a donation to the charity MiracleFeet in lieu of presents for her first birthday presents. At this point, we wanted to do something to help other clubfoot kids in need. We did research about where to donate, and while there are several good clubfoot organizations, we landed on MiracleFeet. Their organization is focused on providing clubfoot treatment for children throughout the world, particularly in third world countries. Their donation process was simple and made it easy for friends and family to donate.

We told MiracleFeet that we were hosting a birthday party and they sent us literature about some of the children they have treated and their progress, stickers, and post cards that we could hand out at the party. The option to host a birthday party can be found on their MiracleFeet donation page. There is also an option to make your donation in honor of someone, so we would receive an email from MiracleFeet from our friends and family who had decided to donate. This was helpful so that we would know that they donated and could thank them later. There are several different donation amounts, and you can choose anything as low as $5.00 or up to $250.00 (the cost to provide full clubfoot correction for one child). We were really impressed with MiracleFeet and their donation process and would recommend them to any family who is interested in doing a donation page as well.

Keep Going

Parenting a child with clubfoot is a lot like parenting in general, in that there is always something different around the corner. Just when you think you have it all figured out and you are in a good routine, your child changes and everything is topsy-turvy again. Caring for your cutie is no different. You have to remain flexible if you want to survive. You have to be able to let go of having control of everything and focus on only the things you can control. You can put your cuties BnB on religiously, no excuses. You can do their physical therapy multiple times a day without fail.

You can do everything in your power to calm and soothe them when they are fussy and not feeling well. You can't control whether your cutie has a relapse even though you have done everything in your power to prevent it. You can't control whether your cutie gets a blister when switching boot sizes, even though you have done everything to try and prevent it. You can remain flexible and adjust your own expectations. You can be more go with the flow. You can acknowledge your own ability to love and care for your cutie in a way you never thought possible. You can know your own strength and resilience while witnessing your cutie's strength and resilience.

If there is one gift my cutie has given me, it is the knowledge that I am more resilient than I ever knew. I struggled night after sleepless night and was able to survive the day. I was able to bounce my baby on an exercise ball until I thought my back would give out while trying to parent my older daughters, too. I was able to research as much as I could about a topic I knew nothing about and turn that knowledge into the best possible care for my child. I did not give up. I survived. I grew and learned more about myself than I ever thought possible. Without my cutie none of this would have happened. I would not be who I am today, and I would never have written this book. This journey will change you. It will make you see things in yourself that you never knew were there. It will make you do things you never thought possible. Embrace the journey. The good, the bad, and the ever changing, and know that you will be changed through it all. After all that is what parenting does — it changes you.

AFTERWORD

I couldn't finish this book without taking the time to thank all the people who have dedicated their lives to clubfoot treatment. Every day I am grateful for Dr. Ponseti who had the vision of how clubfoot treatment could be the least invasive and most successful and made it happen. I am grateful for men like John Mitchell who worked beside Dr. Ponseti to create a boot that would provide the most comfort for clubfoot cuties during their extended wear. I am thankful for the doctors who are currently making advances in treatment through research and outreach like Dr. Dobbs and Dr. Pirani. But I am also equally thankful for all the clubfoot parents who came before me. Without these parents, these moms specifically, clubfoot treatment simply wouldn't be where it is today.

Dr. Ponseti spent his life working on a non-surgical way to treat clubfoot and the medical community was apprehensive about it. They didn't understand how effective the treatment was, and maybe they didn't know how to handle the longevity of the treatment, but for whatever reason the medical community was not buying in to the method. But guess who did buy in to the method? Guess who placed their trust in a doctor who was providing real results for children? You got it, moms.

Dr. Ponseti attributes the rise in the Ponseti method for clubfoot treatment as the premiere treatment option to moms on the internet. At the end of his life, when he should have been retiring after his service to the medical community, Dr. Ponseti ended up performing the Ponseti method for clubfoot treatment more regularly than ever. Why? Because clubfoot moms are persistent. Because clubfoot moms trust their instincts and do whatever it takes to find the best treatment possible for their cuties. These moms saw the results the Ponseti method was delivering through an internet site that Dr. Ponseti had established himself and then they did whatever it took to get their child into the hands of the best clubfoot doctor in the world.

Just take a moment and think about that. Look at your own cutie and think about where they are in the treatment process and how far they have inevitably come and reflect on all the parents who paved the way for them. Did the moms who originally pushed to see Dr. Ponseti know more about his method than the greater medical community? No. Could they give you all the medical outcomes for why using serial casting instead of surgery gave their child a better chance at a pain-free life? Probably not. What they did know is what they felt in their gut. That maternal instinct that kicked in, the one I have talked about several times in this book and they chose to follow it. And thank goodness they did, because where would we be without them?

It amazes me to think of all the moms who came before me, who were willing to be courageous and take a chance on a method that wasn't the most used method in the world. Think of the courage it must have taken to go against what your local doctor was telling you and take a risk. Their courage gives me courage. Their courage paved the way for your courage, too. Those parents' ability to say no, I am not going to do exactly what you tell me to just because you are a doctor, and say I am going to do my own research and make the best possible decision for my child is courageous. They did what they knew was right and it changed the landscape of clubfoot treatment forever. It gave Dr. Ponseti the ability to show what he could do and it helped legitimize his methods for the medical community at large.

I thought a lot about these clubfoot mom warriors during the writing of this book. I pictured them pushing forward, going against the grain, and fighting for a better future for their child. I saw them demanding the best for their child and I tried to do the same with my cutie. The day after my daughter was diagnosed with clubfoot, I knew I had to utilize all my personal strengths to provide her the best possible life. I knew I had to adjust the way I interacted with the medical community, and make decisions about who I trusted to care for my daughter based not their advice but my own instincts, research, and the recommendations of my fellow clubfoot moms. I knew I was going to be pushed out of my comfort zone and have to find the courage to do things I never thought I would.

I pictured those moms who did it before me. Their image helped me to find the strength to switch doctors when I needed to and to research everything I could. Now I encourage you to let their image help you tap into your own courage, strength, and resilience. When you are feeling defeated, exhausted, and confused, picture all those clubfoot moms who came before you and find your own inner resolve to keep going. They stood in the face of fear and said I will not back down until I know that my child will be treated through the best mode of treatment possible. You can do the same. Maybe it won't look exactly the same, but it will take the same resolve to keep going.

This is why I am thankful for the clubfoot parents of the past and of all the clubfoot parents reading this right now. You are so brave and courageous. You are putting in the daily work to ensure that your child's feet stay corrected. Every time you choose to put the BnB on your cutie, you are winning. You make progress every day and you should celebrate that progress because without you, the Ponseti method wouldn't work. Dr. Ponseti knew that. He knew that parents had to buy into the BnB stage of treatment in order for the results to last. So just like all the parents who came before us, we are clubfoot warriors too. In the shadow of their image, we will continue to fight on and make a better future for our children. And just like them, we will pave the way for the clubfoot parents who come after us.

So, what can we do to help the future clubfoot community? How can we pay it forward? How can we follow in those enormous footsteps and create a new path for parents? I think my answer is by creating a supportive community for clubfoot parents around the world. I am envisioning a community where we can connect with each other on a more intimate level. Where we can share our unique experiences with each other in an empathetic and open manner. We all have a story to tell, and there are other moms out there desperate to hear them. Think back to that moment when you first heard the word clubfoot, tap into the emotions you felt, and then picture another mom in your same spot, feeling the same emotions you did. What would you want her to know? What comfort could you provide her about the journey? How could you support her?

To end this book, I wanted to challenge you to share your experience and to pay it forward to the clubfoot community. Whether that looks like keeping those adorable leg warmers in storage and offering them to a fellow clubfoot mom, or contacting a mom who posted on a social media site that their child was just diagnosed and offer her some kind and reassuring words. Maybe it is commenting on a post in the baby-wearing group giving suggestions on the best positions that worked for you, or something larger like sharing your negative or positive experience with a clubfoot doctor with a mom that you know is seeing the same doctor. I challenge you to find a way to pay it forward, because we have seen the power that clubfoot parents can harness and the outcomes they can achieve. We need to do the same for our future selves.

My hope is that by writing this book I have done my part to both pave a new path and encourage you to do the same. I see the future of clubfoot treatment as moving towards more active support for parents who are on the frontlines of care during the BnB phase, both within the medical community and surrounding resources. I want to do my part and enact change by creating a safe place for parents to find support. If you need more active support, whether it be through a blog, a buddy system, a virtual support group, or one-on-one coaching please feel free to go to my website and contact me. I will do everything I can to help you find the support that you need through the resources that are available.

The rise of the Ponseti method of treatment is just one of the many examples of the power we parents have in the decisions we make for our children. It is the example that hits the closest to home for me. I am so thankful for everyone who came before me on the clubfoot path, and for everyone who took the time to read this book. The clubfoot community is lucky to have you on the journey, and your unique perspective will help other parents along their journey if you choose to share it. Keep calm and *brace on!*

My clubfoot cutie on her 1st birthday! This book would not have happened without her. She is the picture of strength, resilience, and grace and we love her to the moon and back.

ACKNOWLEDGMENTS

I would like to thank my husband, Brian, for his unwavering support and encouragement when writing this book, and also to my three girls, who bring the light into my life.

An enormous thank you to the whole team at MDO. A special thank you to Thomas Sharp and Luke Mitchell for seeing the potential in this book and making it happen, and providing it to families in need. Thank you for providing an amazing product in the Mitchell Ponseti® AFO for cuties everywhere and for being a resource for clubfoot parents around the globe. Your generosity is incredible.

A special thank you to Matthew Dobbs, MD for providing his medical expertise and reference material, and for providing the absolute best care a mother could ask for her child.

To my original editor, Laurel VanOrden for providing the support needed to make an idea into reality. My developmental editor, Sydney Argenta, for pushing me to expand on my experience and have confidence in telling my story. To Jill Murphy, Pat Murphy, Conor Murphy, Krista Hugenberg, Emmy Hise, Celeste Labadie, Dr. David Hicks for being my first readers and providing guidance. To my therapist Ben Gaibel, for helping me find my strength in a difficult time. To Tony Hageman, PT, for being a guiding light and consistent resource for us and our daughter. To Gina Navarro and Megan Olson for being my constant rocks on this clubfoot journey, I couldn't picture a better support system to have along the way. Your love and support mean the world to me.

This book is truly for all the parents who are caring for their clubfoot cuties. You inspire me and I am so very proud to be a clubfoot momma, it is very special group!

GLOSSARY OF TERMS

Note: This is the list of terms you will find in this book, or terms that are regularly used in the clubfoot community that you may hear in different areas. It is geared to provide you with a quick go to if you run into a term or acronym that you don't immediately recognize.

Abduction - a motion that pulls away from the midline of the body; movement of a body part away from the median plane

Achilles' Tendon - the tendon that joins the bone of the heel to the calf muscle

Adduction - a motion that pulls toward the midline of the body; movement of a body part toward the median plane

ADM - abduction Dorsiflexion Mechanism

AFO - ankle Foot Orthosis

Anterior - at or towards the front

Anxiety - a state of apprehension and psychic tension caused by distress or uneasiness of mind frequently caused by danger or misfortune

BCF - bilateral clubfoot

Bilateral - both feet affected, pertaining to both sides

Birth Defect - any structural or biochemical abnormality present at birth, may be due to genetic or developmental factors

Blanching - this occurs when the skin becomes white or pale in appearance. You can test the toes of your cutie by pressing down on the red/pinkness of the toes and it should turn white for a couple of seconds before returning to its natural color.

Blisters - a fluid-filled elevation of the skin

CFC - clubfoot Cutie (Cutie)

CFO - custom Foot Orthodics

Congenital - present at birth; existing at and usually before, birth; referring to conditions that are present at birth

Deformity - a distortion of any part of, or the body in general, different in size or shape

Dorsiflexion - flexing the foot in an upward position; movement at the ankle joint that points the foot upwards

Dorsi Ramp - device used to help stretch the Achilles' tendon and calf muscles

Duoderm - a dressing used for the treatment of lightly to moderately draining pressure sores and wounds, waterproof

Eversion - Sole of the foot turns outward

External Rotation - turning outwardly or away from the midline of the body; when toes are pointed away from the body

Idiopathic - arising from an unknown cause; the exact cause unknown

Inversion - toward the midline of the body; turning inward of an anatomical part of the foot

KAFO - knee-ankle Foot Orthosis

LCF - left clubfoot

Manipulation - to stretch and loosen tight structures

MD Orthopaedics - company selling clubfoot products. Website: www.mdortho-paedics.com

Molefoam - helps prevent sores/friction, self-adhesive, cut to size, thicker than moleskin

Moleskin - helps prevent blisters, self-stick adhesive, can be cut to size

Muscle Atrophy - decrease in the mass of the muscle

Occupational Therapy (OT) - treatment of people with physical, emotional, or social problems, using purposeful activity to help them overcome or learn to deal with their problems

Orthotist - primary medical clinician responsible for the prescription, manufacture and management of orthosis

Orthotics - the science that deals with the use of specialized mechanical devices to support or supplement weakened or abnormal joints of limbs

Plantar Flexion - flexing the foot downward, bending foot toward the sole

Plantigrade - walking evenly on the sole of the foot

Podiatry - the study, diagnosis and medical and surgical treatment of disorders of the foot, ankle, and lower extremity

Ponseti Method - a manipulative technique that corrects congenital clubfoot without invasive surgery

Postpartum Anxiety - a mental health state occurring in women after giving birth that can include symptoms such as anxious feelings, extreme stress, racing mind, inability to sleep, imagining worst case scenarios, and fear

Pressure Saddles - (also known as "pringles") chip-shaped item that attaches to the middle strap of the Mitchell Ponseti® boots to provide additional relief from pressure areas

Pressure Sores - Injury to skin and underlying tissue resulting from prolonged pressure on the skin

Pronation - An everting motion of the foot so as to turn the sole outward. The inward roll of the foot during normal motion and occurs as the outer edge of the heel strikes the ground and the foot rolls inward and flattens out. Moderate pronation is required for the foot to function. With excessive pronation, the foot arch flattens out and stretches the muscles, tendons and ligaments underneath the foot

Physical Therapy (PT) - the treatment or management of physical disability, malfunction, or pain by physical techniques, as exercises, massage, hydrotherapy

RCF - right clubfoot

Relapse - the return of ill health after an apparent or partial recovery; reverting back to its original state

Rocker Bottom - an anomaly of the foot, characterized by a prominent heel bone and rounded bottom of the foot; resembling the bottom of a rocking chair; can occur in the case of overcorrection of a clubfoot

Supination - the outward roll of the foot during normal motion. The opposite of pronation, it is the outward roll of the foot during normal motion. A natural amount of supination occurs during the push off phase of running as the heel lifts off the ground and the forefoot and toes are used to propel the body forward

Talipes - the Latin word compounded from talus (ankle) and pes (foot)

Talus - ankle bone; the smaller of the two bones forming the ankle and heel joint

Tenotomy - tendon release, tendon lengthening, heel cord release; the division of the Achilles' tendon

UCF - unilateral clubfoot

Unilateral - one foot is affected

Varus - bent or twisted inward

Vertical Talus - the talus bone has formed in the wrong position and other foot bones to the front of the talus have shifted on top of it. The front of the foot points up and may even rest against the shin

BIBLIOGRAPHY

Books

Cook, T. *Clubfoot: The Quest for a Better Life for Millions of Children*. Iowa: Ice Cube Press, LLC, 2019.

Miller, B. *The Parent's Guide to Clubfoot*. California: Hunter House Inc., 2012.

Reference Material

C-Pro Direct. "ADM Case History." https://c-prodirect.com/Content/Images/uploaded/ADM%20Downloads/casestudies/127_MKT_JDB_v001.pdf.

Dobbs, M., 2020. A Parents Guide Through the Clubfoot Journey. [pdf] Paley Orthopedic and Spine Institute, pp.3-7. Available at: <https://paleyinstitute.org/centers-of-excellence/clubfoot-center/#/> .

Ponseti, I. "Bracing Tips." http://www.ponseti.info/bracing-tips.html.

Ponseti, I. "Casting Care Instructions." http://www.ponseti.info/casting-care-instructions.html(accessed 1 April 2020).

Special Learning Inc. "Depression in Parents of Children with Special Needs: How to Recognize the Symptoms and Signs." https://www.special-learning.com/article/depression.

St. Louis Children's Hospital, Center for Foot Disorders. "Exercises for Clubfoot." https://www.stlouischildrens.org/conditions-treatments/center-foot-disorders/ponseti-method-for-clubfoot/exercises (accessed 1 April 2020).

St. Louis Children's Hospital, Center for Foot Disorders. "Post-casting Care." https://www.stlouischildrens.org/conditions-treatments/center-foot-disorders/ponseti-method-for-clubfoot/post-casting-care(accessed 1 April 2020).

St. Louis Children's Hospital, Center for Foot Disorders. "The Ponseti Method." https://www.stlouischildrens.org/conditions-treatments/center-foot-disorders/ponseti-method-for-clubfoot/treatment(accessed 1 April 2020).

University of Iowa Stead Family Children's Hospital, Orthopedic Surgery. "To Parents of Children Born with Clubfeet." https://uichildrens.org/health-library/parents-children-born-clubfeet (accessed 19 March 2021).

Additional Resources

26th Ave Clubfoot Essentials www.26thaveclubfootessentials.com

Clubfoot CARES. www.clubfootcares.org

The Clubhub. www.clubfoothub.com

MD Orthopaedics. www.mdorthopaedics.com

Miracle Feet. miraclefeet.org

ABOUT THE AUTHOR

Maureen Hoff is the mother of three strong and sassy girls, the third of whom was born with bilateral clubfoot in 2018. She wrote *Clubfoot Chronicles* to help other parents navigate their child's clubfoot journey; and help them find the resources — the answers — they need to succeed.

Maureen understands the importance of self-care in parenting, especially when dealing with the challenges presented by a clubfoot diagnosis. She is a trained life coach and earned her Master's Degree in Marriage and Family Therapy from Regis University in 2012, both of which give her unique insight into the value of maintaining good mental health while parenting.

Maureen currently lives in Colorado with her husband and children. She encourages clubfoot parents to remember — *you are not alone.*

You can contact her at
www.maureenhoff.com
and follow her on social media at
@clubfootchroniclesmom